M140

Introducing statistics

Book 1

Descriptive statistics

This publication forms part of the Open University module M140 *Introducing statistics*. Details of this and other Open University modules can be obtained from Student Recruitment, The Open University, PO Box 197, Milton Keynes MK7 6BJ, United Kingdom (tel. +44 (0)300 303 5303; email general-enquiries@open.ac.uk).

Alternatively, you may visit the Open University website at www.open.ac.uk where you can learn more about the wide range of modules and packs offered at all levels by The Open University.

To purchase a selection of Open University materials visit www.ouw.co.uk, or contact Open University Worldwide, Walton Hall, Milton Keynes MK7 6AA, United Kingdom for a catalogue (tel. +44 (0)1908 274066; fax +44 (0)1908 858787; email ouw-customer-services@open.ac.uk).

The Open University, Walton Hall, Milton Keynes, MK7 6AA.

First published 2013. Second edition 2015.

Edited, designed and typeset by The Open University, using the Open University TeX System.

Printed in the United Kingdom by Page Bros, Norwich.

ISBN 978 1 4730 0305 7

2.1

Contents

Unit 1   Looking for patterns   1

Introduction   3

1   Studying M140   4
     1.1   The module components   5
     1.2   Studying effectively   6

2   Patterns in data   6
     2.1   The statistical modelling diagram   7
     2.2   Making use of patterns in data   11
     Exercises on Section 2   15

3   Preparing the data for analysis   16
     3.1   Cleaning the data   16
     3.2   Rounding   20
     3.3   Calculating from the table   24
     Exercises on Section 3   28

4   Pictures of data   29
     4.1   Stemplots   30
     4.2   The median and the range   35
     Exercises on Section 4   41

5   The shape of a batch   42
     5.1   How many levels?   42
     5.2   Peaks and symmetry   47
     Exercises on Section 5   55

6   Computer work: introducing Minitab   56

7   Completing the assignments   56
     7.1   Answering iCMA questions   57
     7.2   Answering TMA questions   58

Summary   64

Learning outcomes   65

Solutions to activities   66

Solutions to exercises   76

Acknowledgements   81

Contents

Unit 2 Prices	**83**
Introduction	**85**
1 Measuring location	**86**
1.1 Data on prices	87
1.2 The median	88
1.3 The arithmetic mean	92
1.4 The mean and median compared	93
Exercises on Section 1	96
2 Weighted means	**97**
2.1 The mean of a combined batch	97
2.2 Further uses of weighted means	100
2.3 More than two numbers	105
Exercises on Section 2	109
3 Measuring spread	**110**
3.1 The range	110
3.2 Quartiles and the interquartile range	111
3.3 The five-figure summary and boxplots	118
Exercises on Section 3	124
4 A simple chained price index	**125**
4.1 A two-commodity price index	126
Exercises on Section 4	132
5 The UK government price indices	**132**
5.1 What are the CPI and RPI?	133
5.2 Calculating the price indices	139
5.3 Using the price indices	144
Exercises on Section 5	150
6 Computer work: measures of location	**151**
Summary	**151**
Learning outcomes	**152**
Solutions to activities	**153**
Solutions to exercises	**163**
Acknowledgements	**167**

Unit 3	**Earnings**	**169**
Introduction		**171**
1	**Gender and earnings**	**172**
1.1	Posing the question	172
1.2	Comparing earnings of men and women	174
1.3	The Annual Survey of Hours and Earnings	178
1.4	Averages: the mean or the median?	179
1.5	Deciles	186
1.6	Earnings ratios across the distribution	191
1.7	Has the 'gap' between men's and women's earnings been closing?	193
1.8	Further investigations into gender and earnings	194
	Exercises on Section 1	197
2	**Boxplots and skewness**	**198**
2.1	Recognising skewness	198
2.2	Boxplots: the details	201
	Exercises on Section 2	206
3	**Comparing batches**	**208**
3.1	The standard deviation	208
3.2	Calculating the mean and standard deviation for grouped data	217
3.3	Deciding which measure to use	222
	Exercises on Section 3	223
4	**Computer work: summary measures and boxplots**	**224**
5	**Prices and earnings**	**224**
5.1	The Average Weekly Earnings (AWE) index	225
5.2	Comparing the AWE with the CPI	227
5.3	Points to consider when using the AWE	232
Summary		**235**
Learning outcomes		**236**
Solutions to activities		**237**
Solutions to exercises		**249**
Acknowledgements		**253**
Index		**255**

Unit 1

Looking for patterns

Introduction

Welcome to M140! This module is about using data, usually in the form of numbers, to describe aspects of society and the environment so that we can understand, interpret and, on occasion, change the world around us.

Statistics is a broad discipline, touching virtually all aspects of social and scientific activity. For example, many items in the news relate in some way to statistical questions, often with direct relevance to our own lives:

A dictionary definition of statistics is: 'a science concerned with the collection, classification and interpretation of quantitative data'.

- Are average house prices going up or down in my area?

- How should I interpret league tables for choosing a school?

- Have the traffic control measures implemented in my town reduced car accidents?

- How is my pension calculated and how much can I expect to get?

- How safe and effective are the medical treatments I have been prescribed?

These questions, or others like them, might concern you – and all have a statistical component.

More generally, and on a much larger scale, statistical data are used to monitor the health of populations, the levels of development and inequality, climate change and the performance of global markets. Figure 1 shows one such use of statistics. The purpose of this module is to introduce you to the use of data in a variety of different situations, to enable you to take a more informed view of statistical data and statistical reasoning, and to teach you some of the statistical techniques that are used to make sense of data.

The word 'data' is regarded as plural. One observation is a 'datum'.

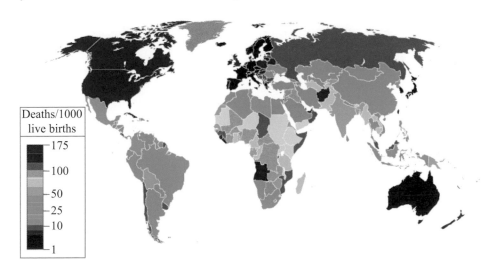

Figure 1 World infant mortality rates (2008)

Figure 2 The wheatsheaf emblem

Threshing the data

The scope of statistics was the topic of some debate in the early days of the discipline. In 1834, the Statistical Society of London was founded, with a wheatsheaf as its emblem. This was inscribed with the Latin motto '*aliis exterendum*', translated as 'to be threshed by others', though the accuracy of this translation has since been disputed. This was interpreted to mean that while statisticians collect and present data (the wheat, in this analogy), they should leave the interpretation of data (the threshing) to others. This was hotly disputed at the time, the opposing view – generally accepted by modern statisticians – being that statistics also involves interpreting and drawing inferences from data. Eventually, the Latin motto was dropped. The Royal Statistical Society, which succeeded the Statistical Society of London, still uses the wheatsheaf as its emblem, shown in Figure 2.

The teaching method we have adopted for the whole module is that statistics is best learned by *doing* rather than by *reading*. For this reason, this introduction has been kept short!

However, this being the introductory unit, we thought it useful to begin in Section 1 with a brief overview of the study materials and how to use them. In Section 2 we describe in general terms the process of statistical modelling. In Section 3 you will learn how to look critically at data, prepare it for further analysis, and undertake simple calculations. Sections 4 and 5 develop some simple tools for looking at data, and summarising some key aspects of a batch of data.

Sections 1 to 5 of the unit will require only pen, paper and a calculator, and you should have these at hand throughout. However, for handling larger datasets, and producing good graphs, a computer is essential. In Section 6 you will learn how to use the statistical package Minitab, including how to print/paste output for your assignments. So you will need access to your computer for that section.

Finally, Section 7 provides some advice and practice for the module assessments. Some of this will involve accessing online questions, so you will need access to the internet for this section.

1 Studying M140

This section contains some guidance on how to make the most effective use of the study materials and other resources. The M140 Guide also provides general guidance on studying the module, and you should read through this before you start Section 2.

1.1 The module components

Central to the module is the M140 website, where you will find copies of the M140 materials, the study planner, screencasts (audio–visual clips), practice quizzes, assessments and other information. It is worth checking the website regularly (say, once a week) for updates, news and corrections, and to drop in on the module forums to interact with other students.

The module software is provided separately on a CD.

Most of your studying will be based on the M140 units. Each unit of M140 is structured in a similar way. New ideas are illustrated by examples, and followed by activities for you to work through. Some of the new ideas are also demonstrated in the screencasts on the M140 website. The best way to learn statistics is to do it yourself, so it is important to work through the activities as you study the units. There are also exercises, usually given at the end of a section, which are there to give you extra practice should you feel you need it, and you can test your understanding of a unit by working through its associated practice quiz on the M140 website.

The Handbook contains some of the key ideas and formulas taught in M140, along with some useful statistical tables. You may find it helpful to keep the Handbook close by as you study the units, and add your own notes or examples so that it becomes a convenient source of reference. Finding your way round the Handbook is easier than searching through the units, and using it to look up material from earlier units might come in useful at a later stage.

The Computer Book will guide you through the use of the module software, mainly through activities. The module software work will involve using the statistical package Minitab. The Computer Book also contains activities that use interactive computer resources on the M140 website, which are designed to reinforce ideas in the units.

In the module material, there are icons to indicate where you will need to use the Computer Book, your calculator or an online resource. The corresponding icon for each of these is displayed here, from left to right. You might find these icons useful to plan your work, as you can see at a glance at which point these resources will be required.

The online work will include the screencasts and interactive computer resources, and you will be guided to the relevant ones as you work through the module material. The screencasts provide further demonstration of particular concepts and you may wish to review each of these straight after the relevant module material, or perhaps all together later on. The interactive computer resources are to be used with the relevant activities in the Computer Book.

Section 6 directs you to the parts in the Computer Book relevant to Unit 1. Note that you are also guided to part of the Computer Book at the end of Section 2, as you can choose to work through it at this point if you like. Section 7 of this unit will give you some information on working through the interactive computer-marked assignments (iCMAs), using the practice quizzes and answering questions in tutor-marked assignments (TMAs).

1.2 Studying effectively

The key to studying effectively is to plan your study time well ahead, and ensure you make suitable adjustments to fit your study into your life.

Each unit is designed to take about 16 hours of study. This includes studying the unit (and any associated work in the Computer Book), reviewing the relevant screencasts, attempting the practice quiz and doing some of the end-of-section exercises. Some units may take you longer than others. You will need to allow some extra time for doing the assessment questions, and for other activities such as tutorials. It is important that you keep up with the study schedule in the study planner, which is on the M140 website, or you may find that you have run out of time to read the relevant units needed to complete an assignment by its cut-off date. So it's worth you trying to plan your study times, to fit them in with your other commitments, to make sure that you do not fall behind.

As you work through the units, it helps to have pen and paper ready to try out calculations for yourself, check you agree with the results in the unit, and to keep notes more generally. Remember, this module is all about *doing* statistics, not just *reading* about the subject.

It is important to remember that you are not alone with the study materials. Your tutor is there to help you with any statistical problems that you encounter. You should also raise with your tutor any matters to do with your progress, such as what you should do if you are worried that you may not complete an assignment or part of the module on time.

The module forums are another place where you can seek help, and also give help to others. If there's something you don't understand, then spend a few minutes on it, make a note of it and perhaps return to it later. (You may find that it becomes clearer the second time round.) You could also see if one of the screencasts is relevant to whatever you are unsure about, as you may find it helpful to watch an example being worked through. But don't spend too much time puzzling over something without making progress. One step you can usefully take is to look on the module forums to see if any other students have met the same problem, and how they resolved it. You can also post your own query on a forum, or contact your tutor, and continue studying the rest of the unit in the meantime.

Jessica had to resort to extreme measures to find the time and space to study

2 Patterns in data

The whole of M140 is about statistical modelling. In this section, the process is introduced in very general terms.

2.1   The statistical modelling diagram

In M140 you are going to spend a good deal of time looking at collections of numbers. Sometimes the data may display **patterns** that are incomplete or not immediately obvious. The objective will be to describe the pattern in each case and then, with the help of this description, to attempt to interpret this pattern in the context in which it occurs. The interpretation will often involve examining what the numbers suggest about a particular situation, and will sometimes enable us to make useful predictions about it. Sometimes you will find that what may have appeared to be a pattern was just a chance occurrence!

Here is a simple and familiar example to illustrate how patterns in data can be interpreted in context. More complex data and contexts will be introduced later.

Example 1   *House numbers*

Suppose that you are walking down a road and you observe that six consecutive houses on one side of the road are numbered 1, 3, 5, 7, 9, 11. You stop and ask yourself what number the next house will be.

Observations such as the house numbers of Example 1 are called **data** and the process of making **observations** is called **data collection**. Taken as a whole, the numbers 1, 3, 5, 7, 9, 11 are called a **batch of data** or a **dataset**.

In Example 1 you have done two things.

- You have **posed a precise question** to be answered: what is the number of the seventh house?

- You have **collected some data**, namely, the numbers of the first six houses: 1, 3, 5, 7, 9, 11. You hope to be able to use these observations to solve the problem.

The problem will be solved when a prediction has been made. To make this prediction, you need to complete a third task.

- You must **analyse the data** and see if you can find a pattern.

You have probably done this already and got the answer 13 because this number fits the obvious pattern. In doing this you may have used the rule 'the next house number is the next odd number in the sequence'. This rule describes the systematic pattern which, you believe, underlies the data: it is an example of a **model**. The tasks 'pose a precise question', 'collect some data' and 'analyse the data' are important stages in the modelling process.

Activity 1 *Predicting the next house number*

Can you *guarantee* that the next house in Example 1 will be numbered 13? Explain your answer.

What you have done in the solution to Activity 1 is another important stage in the modelling process.

- You have **interpreted the model**.

In doing so, you did not just look at the pattern of the numbers. You also used your knowledge of what the numbers actually represented, that is, the fact that they were house numbers. This knowledge helps to interpret the pattern in the right 'real-world' context and in this case to suggest why the model might not apply to all the house numbers. It is essential to know the 'real-world' meaning of the numbers in a batch in order to interpret the data.

The four stages of the modelling process highlighted here are summarised in Figure 3.

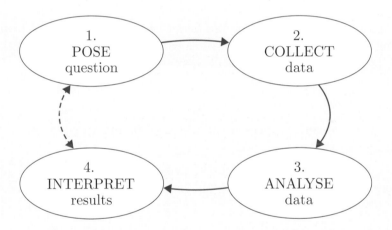

Figure 3   The modelling diagram

The **modelling diagram** will be referred to throughout this unit, and on many occasions throughout the module. This unit is concerned mainly with stage 3 – *analyse data* – particularly with the search for patterns in the data. However, the other stages will occasionally be mentioned.

It has already been said that an analysis should lead to a pattern from which predictions can be made. The pattern for the house numbers is that they are the odd whole numbers taken in ascending order. Normally, data will not exhibit such a clear regular pattern as that of the house numbers. The following example is more typical.

In fact, the house number example does not quite fit the modelling diagram since the question arose only after looking at the data – sometimes it needs some data to stimulate a question! The modelling diagram is really intended to cover the more systematic approach where the question posed comes first.

Example 2 *Impact of fertiliser use on grain yield*

Table 1 contains some data from an agricultural experiment to investigate the effect of fertiliser on the amount of wheat-grain produced. Let us presume that the question posed was:

> *How is grain yield affected by how much fertiliser is used?*

and that the experiment was done to try and answer this question.

The 'pose' icon, based on Figure 3, is used to emphasise that this corresponds to the first stage of the modelling diagram. This and similar icons will appear at suitable points to emphasise which step of the modelling diagram is involved.

Table 1   Fertiliser use and grain yield

Fertiliser use (kg/ha)	0	25	50	75	100	125
Grain yield (tonnes/ha)	4.27	4.67	5.00	5.03	5.28	5.67

In this example we are interested in making predictions about how much grain might be produced by a given application of fertiliser. Specifically, we would like to know what would happen if *intermediate* quantities of fertiliser were used, such as 35 or 90 kg/ha, lying between the values for which the experiment was conducted.

Have a look at Figure 4, where we have plotted the data from Table 1. The quantity of fertiliser used (in kg/ha) is indicated horizontally and the grain yield (in tonnes/ha) is indicated vertically. Each experimental result is marked with a point, or dot.

This type of plot is called a **scatterplot**, as it helps to visualise a pattern (or lack of any pattern) in the scatter of data on the page.

As you can see, the six points are roughly in a straight line. In Figure 5 we have drawn a straight line on the graph; this line represents a possible model for the data, which represents the observed pattern.

1. Pose

2. Collect

Here 'kg/ha' means that the fertiliser was measured in kilogrammes per hectare.

3. Analyse

In Unit 5 you will learn how to obtain such lines.

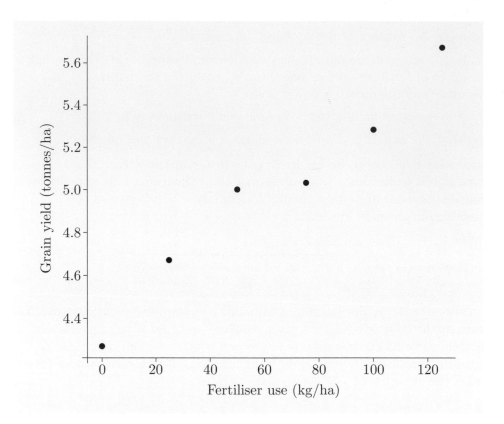

Figure 4   Grain yield by fertiliser use

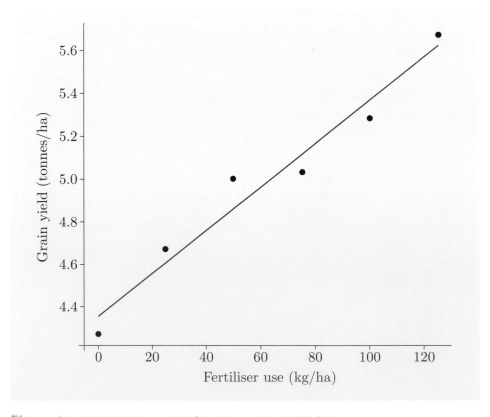

Figure 5   A possible model for the grain yield data

The straight-line graph represents a way of guessing a value of the grain yield from a value of the fertiliser use. This can be expressed by the simple formula:

Grain yield in tonnes/ha $= 4.35 + 0.01 \times$ (Fertiliser use in kg/ha).

A value of the grain yield obtained from this formula can be regarded as a 'good guess' at what the value of the grain yield might have been for any particular quantity of fertiliser, if that amount of fertiliser had actually been used in the experiment. In this sense, it can be regarded as a **prediction** – actually a prediction about what might have happened at the time of the experiment, not about the future! For instance, for 35 kg/ha the formula predicts a yield of $4.35 + (0.01 \times 35)$, which equals 4.70 tonnes/ha, and for 90 kg/ha it predicts a yield of $4.35 + (0.01 \times 90)$, which equals 5.25 tonnes/ha. These should be good guesses at what might have been achieved in practice in these cases.

However, for 50 kg/ha the formula predicts a yield of 4.85 tonnes/ha and for 100 kg/ha it predicts a yield of 5.35 tonnes/ha. These two predictions from the formula are clearly not exact because you can see from Table 1 that the actual yields were 5.00 and 5.28 tonnes/ha respectively. In general, predictions from the formula are not likely to be exact, but you can see from Figure 5 that the straight line is quite close to the data points and gives quite a good summary of the pattern in the data. However, it might not summarise the true situation so well for quantities of fertiliser lying outside the range of data here.

You will learn how to calculate this type of formula in Unit 5.

4. Interpret

Example 2 is the subject of Screencast 1 for Unit 1 (see the M140 website).

2.2   Making use of patterns in data

In this subsection, the process of statistical modelling depicted in Figure 3 is illustrated by an example about *biodiversity*. Biodiversity is the variety of species of different living organisms that inhabit the Earth. This is often used as an indicator of the health of an ecosystem, such as that represented in Figure 6. Therefore, it is of great interest to scientists to find out how many species of a particular plant or animal there are within a particular environment. The task is not easy, because in addition to the species we know about, there may be other species out there that we do not know about; new species are being discovered all the time.

Figure 6   A coral reef teeming with life

1. Pose

2. Collect

3. Analyse

Example 3   *How many large creatures are there in the sea?*

This example is about the number of species of large creatures that live in the sea, where 'large' refers to a length of 2 metres or more for an adult. Thus the question of interest is:

How many large marine species are there?

One way to tackle this rather tricky question is to assemble data on the species discovered so far. The dataset used here lists the total numbers of large marine species so far discovered, in each year between 1829 and 1996. For example, in 1829 there were 101 large marine species known about; by 1996 the number was 217. (Source: Paxton, C.G.M. (1998) 'A cumulative species description curve for large open water marine animals', *Journal of the Marine Biological Association*, vol. 78, pp. 1389–1391.)

The next step is to plot these data, using a scatterplot, to see if a pattern is revealed. This plot is given in Figure 7.

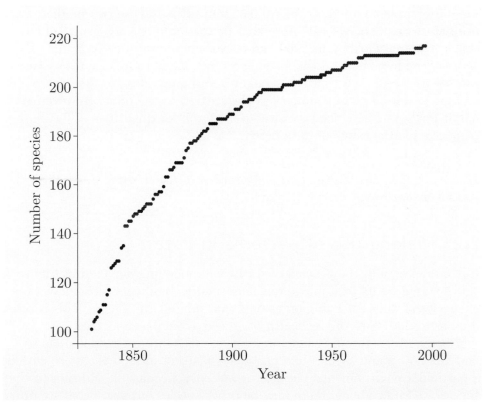

Figure 7   Number of large species discovered by year

You will obtain this plot using Minitab in Section 6.

The years from 1829 to 1996 are indicated horizontally, and the cumulative numbers of species known about by the end of each year (including those discovered that same year) are indicated vertically. This scatterplot is called the *discovery curve* for large marine species.

Figure 7 shows the numbers increasing each year, which is expected since a species known about one year will still be known about the following year. Also, while there are some wiggles in the curve formed by the points, it does appear to be quite smooth.

Activity 2   *Interpreting the discovery curve: 1*

Discuss briefly the following points relating to the pattern of the discovery curve in Figure 7.

(a) Is the discovery curve becoming more steep or less steep as time goes on?

(b) What reasons might there be for the change in steepness?

(c) What do you think might happen in the future (i.e. after 1996), based on the observations so far? What would you expect to happen?

In Example 2, a straight line provided an adequate representation of the fertiliser use and grain yield data. Here, a curved line is indicated for the discovery curve. One possible model for the data is shown in Figure 8.

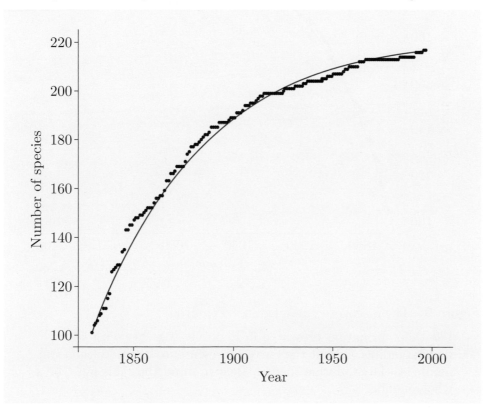

Figure 8   A possible model for the discovery curve

It is not the only such model for these data. How the model was chosen and fitted to the points is not important at this stage.

This model has been chosen so that the curve flattens out as time goes on, as would be expected with such data. The model goes through the data reasonably well, so it provides an adequate representation of the pattern in the data.

The final stage is to interpret the model in the context of the original question. This is the topic of the next activity.

4. Interpret

Activity 3   *Interpreting the discovery curve: 2*

The curve predicts the numbers of species known about each year, and flattens out in the future. In Figure 9, the curve has been drawn as before, but extended until 2100, by which time it is nearly flat. The curve flattens out at a maximum value of 222.94, as indicated on the figure.

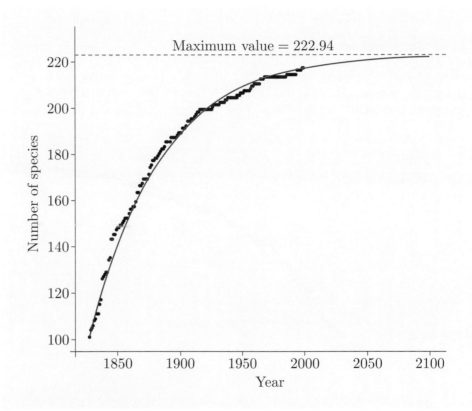

Figure 9   The discovery curve extended to 2100

(a) Use the information presented in Figure 9, together with your understanding of what the curve represents, to estimate the total number of large marine species. Bear in mind that this must be a whole number.

(b) In 1996 there were 217 large marine species known about. How many remained to be discovered?

(c) Briefly discuss what might happen if the curve through the points were changed slightly.

The yeti crab

New creatures are being discovered all the time. In 2005, the yeti crab (*Kiwa hirsuta*), shown in Figure 10, was discovered about 900 miles from Easter Island in the southeastern Pacific Ocean, by scientists working on the Census of Marine Life. It represents an entirely new family of marine organisms.

Figure 10   The yeti crab

In this section, you have learned about the process of statistical modelling, in general terms, through several contrasting examples. In particular, the modelling diagram will crop up throughout M140.

Exercises on Section 2

At the end of each section, you will usually find a few exercises to practise the skills you have learned. Unlike the activities within the sections, which you should work through as you come to them, you may find it helpful to leave working through these exercises until later – for example, when you are revising the unit.

Exercise 1   *Your household budget*

Statistical modelling is not limited to scientific investigations; it arises in everyday life as well.

Suppose that the question you have posed is:

> *How can I reduce my monthly household expenditure?*

Write down what you might do to answer it, using the stages in the modelling diagram: Collect data, Analyse data, and Interpret results. That is, decide what data you would assemble, how you would analyse them, and how you would interpret your results to develop a plan for reducing your future expenditure.

Exercise 2   *More interpretation of the discovery curve*

Figure 8 shows the discovery curve, and a model for it, for large marine species. The curve becomes gradually less steep as time goes on.

(a) Interpret this pattern in terms of the average time between successive discoveries of large marine species, and how this average time varies with each new discovery.

(b) How, in general terms, might the interpretation from part (a) be used to predict the date by which the next large marine species might be discovered? How reliable would such predictions be?

You are now in a position to look at the Introduction to the Computer Book.

3 Preparing the data for analysis

There is an important preliminary part of data analysis which we have so far overlooked. It is not always possible to present data initially in such a neat and tidy fashion as we did in Section 2, particularly if the modelling diagram has not been followed and the data have not actually been gathered in a systematic way to answer a previously posed question. In practice, statisticians often have to use data that have been gathered with different (or no particular) aims in mind. A batch of data of this sort can contain errors, be incomplete in various ways and generally be 'not ready for immediate analysis'. It may even be slightly inappropriate for the questions asked of it. Some of these problems can occur even if the modelling diagram is being followed, but the problems are then usually 'accidental' in nature and should be less serious. Some of the problems can be corrected – others cannot. In this section, we consider some of the tools used for getting the data ready for analysis and some of the key issues relating to accuracy of the data.

3.1 Cleaning the data

The process of doing what you can to get the data ready for analysis is often referred to as **cleaning the data**.

2. Collect

Example 4 *Petrol consumption and expenditure*

For over 15 years, since acquiring his 1996 Honda Civic 1.4i, and with no particular reason in mind, a member of the module team noted down some information every time he filled the car's tank with petrol. He noted down the date, mileage, amount of petrol (in litres), cost per litre (in pence), and overall cost (in pounds sterling: £). At each petrol stop, the tank was completely filled up. Table 2 gives the data for the 2 years running up to the writing of this unit in early 2012; the dates in column two are in day.month.year format.

Table 2 Petrol consumption and expenditure data, Jan. 2010–Jan. 2012

Stop no.	Date	Mileage (miles)	Petrol used (litres)	Petrol price (pence per litre)	Expenditure (£)
1	18.01.10	112 350	46.01	109.9	50.57
2	18.02.10	112 616	44.98	110.9	49.89
3	04.03.10	112 954	43.49	111.9	48.67
4	24.03.10	113 269	45.13	115.9	52.—
5	20.04.10	113 564	41.76	119.9	50.07
6	—.05.10	113 857	44.25	119.9	53.06
7	—.06.10	114 123	40.70	116.9	47.58
8	—.06.10	114 469	43.38	119.9	52.01
9	05.07.10	114 823	41.60	115.9	48.21
10	11.08.10	115 091	41.17	112.9	46.48
11	27.09.10	115 360	45.83	112.9	51.75
12	09.10.10	115 706	43.14	114.9	49.57
13	02.11.10	115 984	44.26	115.9	51.30
14	25.11.10	116 202	37.95	116.9	44.37
15	06.12.10	116 542	45.30	119.9	54.31
16	24.12.10	116 795	40.88	121.9	49.84
17	10.01.11	117 071	37.49	126.9	47.58
18	22.01.11	117 417	44.89	126.9	56.97
19	02.02.11	117 736	40.59	126.9	51.52
20	10.02.11	118 030	33.02	126.9	41.90
21	17.02.11	118 368	42.87	129.9	55.69
22	25.02.11	118 748	47.47	126.9	60.25
23	04.04.11	119 064	36.—	129.9	47.70
24	11.04.11	119 419	41.57	130.9	54.42
25	20.04.11	119 773	45.53	132.9	60.51
26	01.05.11	120 134	43.75	134.9	59.02
27	11.05.11	120 481	37.51	133.9	50.23
28	20.05.11	120 794	40.37	13–.–	54.06
29	06.06.11	121 146	41.98	132.9	55.78
30	23.06.11	121 476	40.86	134.9	55.12
31	07.07.11	121 793	39.78	132.9	52.88
32	27.07.11	122 128	43.2–	132.9	57.43
33	08.10.11	122 436	38.87	131.9	51.27
34	03.11.11	122 786	40.47	128.7	52.08
35	19.01.12	123 108	44.97	130.9	58.87

(The numbers in the first column, 'Stop no.', in Table 2 are not really data but are used to number the rows of the table for easy reference. '—' indicates that digits are missing.)

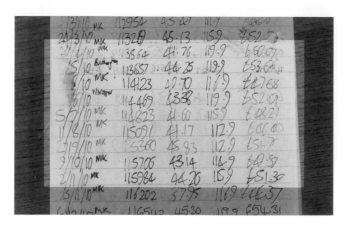

Figure 11   Notebook of data

The data in Table 2 present a few problems. In the 'Date' column the days in rows 6, 7 and 8, corresponding to stop numbers 6, 7 and 8, are missing: the notebook (see Figure 11) in which the records were kept got wet, and part of the entries written close to the edge of the page were illegible – there is nothing we can do about that, though we do know they were in May and June 2010.

The 'Mileage' column is complete. Some entries in the other three columns were partly illegible. This was the case for 'Expenditure' in row 4, 'Petrol price' in row 28, and 'Petrol used' in rows 23 and 32. Nevertheless, since the three quantities ('Petrol used', 'Petrol price' and 'Expenditure') are related, the missing entries can be recovered.

Activity 4   *Calculating the expenditure*

The relationship between 'Petrol used', 'Petrol price' and 'Expenditure' in Table 2 is given by:

$$\text{Expenditure } (\pounds) = \frac{\text{Petrol used (litres)} \times \text{Petrol price (pence per litre)}}{100},$$

where the division by 100 is to convert pence into pounds. Given this relationship, use your calculator to obtain the expenditure corresponding to row 4, as accurately as your calculator permits.

The answer obtained for the converted price for row 4, namely £52.305 67, would look a little odd if inserted directly into Table 2 as it would have three more decimal places than the other values in the column! All this extra accuracy would be wasted when comparing these numbers with the others in the same column.

It is common in mathematics to refer to this sort of accuracy as 'precision'. However, in this module, we use the two terms interchangeably.

In addition, the extra accuracy is probably unjustified because the original data had only four digits in it.

Finally, the extra accuracy is unjustified in this context because the smallest unit of money is a penny, so it makes little sense here to quote all those decimal places. Thus, introducing all these extra decimal places would be to introduce **spurious accuracy** (or *spurious precision*), and that should be avoided.

Another type of spurious accuracy is to claim that a very precise statement is really meaningful, as in the following example.

Context is important here: exchange rates between currencies are often quoted to many decimal places, in order to convert large amounts accurately.

Example 5   *Route planner*

A popular online route planner gives the length of the fastest road route from Milton Keynes to Edinburgh as 342.20 miles, with an estimated travel time of 5 hours 31 minutes and 56 seconds.

Leaving aside the unusual (though scenic) route selected through the Scottish Borders (Figure 12), the overall distance is given to an accuracy of a hundredth of a mile, or about 16 metres, and the travel time to an accuracy of a second. Given the variation in distance and time according to which lanes you use, not to mention other factors such as traffic and weather conditions, this degree of accuracy is hardly realistic, and is not particularly helpful. In practice the most useful information you would probably take from this is that the distance is about 340 miles, with a travel time of about $5\frac{1}{2}$ hours.

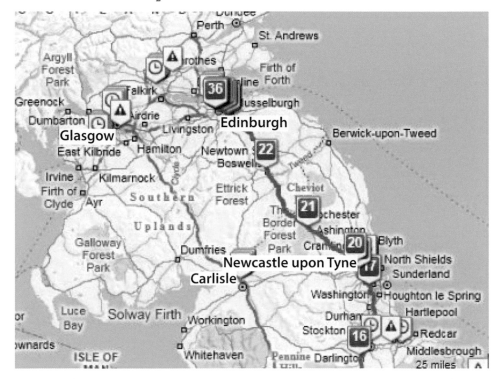

Figure 12   The last part of the recommended route from Milton Keynes to Edinburgh

As with the calculation described in Activity 4, the distance and time in Example 5 should be given to a suitable degree of accuracy to avoid giving a false impression. The next subsection discusses 'rounding' in order to achieve this.

3.2   Rounding

Rounding is used to give a value to a specified degree of accuracy. For example, if we wish to describe the petrol price (per litre) of 109.9 pence in Table 2 in terms of whole pence, the best approximation is clearly 110 pence (equivalently, £1.10) rather than 109 pence, 100 pence (£1.00) or any other value. Similarly, the price 110.9 pence in terms of whole pence is best described as 111 pence (or £1.11) rather than 110 pence or any other value. You can think of this approximation as being 'to the nearest penny'.

In M140 we shall use the following rule for rounding. (In other settings different rules are sometimes used.)

Rounding a number

To round a number, find the digit immediately to the right of where you want to round.

Round up if this digit is 5 or more, and round down otherwise.

Example 6   *Round and round we go*

Suppose we want to round 3.421 3604 to four decimal places. This is done as follows. We want to keep four decimal places, so we want to round at the position indicated by the vertical bar:

$$3.421\,3|604.$$

The digit to the right of where we want to round is 6. Since this is equal to or greater than 5, we round up to 3.4214. Similarly, 3.421 3604 rounded to six decimal places is 3.421 360.

The final zero is retained in 3.421 360 to show that we have rounded to six decimal places rather than to five decimal places.

Rounding before the decimal point is done in the same way. For example, if we want to round 176 354.67 to the nearest thousand, the position we wish to round to is indicated by the vertical bar:

$$176\,|\,354.67,$$

and the digit to the right of where we want to round is 3. Since this is less than 5, we round down to 176 000.

Example 6 is the subject of Screencast 2 for Unit 1 (see the M140 website).

The following activity involves rounding to avoid spurious accuracy.

Activity 5 *The population of the world*

In February 2012, surfing the internet for 'World population on 1st January 2012' produced one website that claimed:

> *As of January 1st, 2012, the population of the world was approximately 6 985 119 415 (6.99 billion).*

Clearly, a count of everybody on the planet was not undertaken instantaneously as the clock struck midnight in every time zone, so we can be confident that the number 6 985 119 415 is spuriously accurate (as acknowledged by the 'approximately' qualifying it).

(a) Round this population count to the nearest million.

(b) To what accuracy is the rounded value '6.99 billion', or 6 990 000 000, given in the quote? Is this value rounded up or down?

Rounding up – as practised in sheep-dog trials

Having practised rounding, it is time to round the values obtained in Activity 4, as this is what led us to consider the issue of accuracy in the first place.

Activity 6 *Rounding the fuel consumption data*

(a) Round the value obtained in Activity 4 to fit the values in the rest of the 'Expenditure' column in Table 2.

(b) Use the relationship between 'Petrol used', 'Petrol price' and 'Expenditure' given in Activity 4 to obtain the value for 'Petrol price' in row 28, and round it to fit the values in that column.

(c) Similarly, obtain the values of 'Petrol used' in rows 23 and 32, and round them to fit the values in that column.

These rounded values can now be written into the appropriate places in Table 2.

We have now completed the missing values in columns 'Petrol used', 'Petrol price' and 'Expenditure' of Table 2 and, since that was all we could actually do, the table has been cleaned up as far as it can be. All the numbers in any particular column are presented to the same degree of accuracy, so no further rounding is required. We shall assume that the degree of accuracy – no more and no less – is justified in every case. The only problems we are left with are some missing dates that we cannot resolve.

Before moving on to performing new calculations from the data, there is one issue which deserves comment, and that is the impact of 'rounding errors'.

The symbol $\simeq$ means 'approximately equal to'. The symbol $\approx$ can also be used.

Example 7   *Rounding error*

If you apply the equation from Activity 4 to, say, the first row of Table 2, and calculate 'Expenditure' from the values provided for 'Petrol used' and 'Petrol price', and round the result to two decimal places, you get

$$\frac{46.01 \times 109.9}{100} = 50.564\,99 \simeq 50.56.$$

This differs in the last decimal place from the entry for 'Expenditure' in row 1 of the table, which is 50.57. This is probably not due to a mistake in the data (though of course it could be), but is most likely due to a **rounding error**. The values for the price of petrol and the amount of petrol purchased that have been entered in Table 2 are most likely rounded values, and this is the reason for the slight discrepancy. For example, if the actual amount of petrol purchased was not 46.01 litres, but 46.014 litres, then the calculation would have been

$$\frac{46.014 \times 109.9}{100} = 50.569\,386 \simeq 50.57.$$

This now matches the value of 'Expenditure' in the table. However, the value of 'Petrol used', rounded to two decimal places, would still be 46.01.

Slight discrepancies due to rounding, typically only affecting the last digit, are frequent in tables, and are nothing to worry about. Large discrepancies, on the other hand, might indicate more serious errors. In calculating quantities to put into a table, it is important to reduce rounding errors to a minimum.

> **Reducing rounding errors**
>
> To reduce rounding errors in the final result, the full accuracy available should be kept in intermediate calculations, and the result should be rounded at the end.

Of course, you might be interested in the result of an intermediate calculation in its own right, in which case you should use the rounded value for that purpose, but still use the full accuracy to complete the calculation. The following activity illustrates what might go wrong if you round too early in a calculation, rather than keep the full accuracy available and round the final output.

Activity 7   *A big rounding error*

Calculate 19.4×23.4 and round the answer to a whole number. Next, round 19.4 and 23.4 to whole numbers first, then multiply them. What do you observe? Which result is correct?

In Activity 7, the rounding error 'grew' in the second calculation. In practice, the numbers you start with often include some rounding error, therefore it is important to know how to handle this in calculations so that the final result is not grossly inaccurate. The issue of how to handle numerical accuracy in calculations will be discussed further in the next subsection.

False security: a costly rounding error

During the first Gulf War, an American Patriot missile system (Figure 13) in Saudi Arabia failed to intercept an incoming Iraqi missile. The missile destroyed an American Army barracks, killing 28 soldiers and leaving many wounded. The cause of the failure of the missile system was eventually tracked down to a rounding error in the system's internal clock, which grew as time went on.

Figure 13   A Patriot missile

3.3 Calculating from the table

What can we actually calculate easily from the data in Table 2? One obvious question of interest is how expensive the car is to run.

This depends on fuel price and distance travelled, but also on the petrol consumption of the car. The next few activities and examples will take you through the steps required to calculate petrol consumption.

In the UK, petrol consumption is calculated from the following formula:

$$\text{Petrol consumption (miles per gallon)} = \frac{\text{Distance travelled (miles)}}{\text{Petrol used (gallons)}}.$$

(In other countries, fuel consumption is often calculated in metric units, frequently in litres per 100 kilometres, which corresponds more accurately to the meaning of 'consumption'.)

To begin with, note that from the mileage values in Table 2 we can certainly work out how many miles the car went between any two stops for petrol.

Activity 8   *Distance travelled*

How far did the car go in the month between 18.01.10 and 18.02.10?
Use your calculator.

Note that we have departed from the modelling diagram in Figure 3, as the data were collected prior to posing the question. This can mean that the data you have are not ideal for answering the question you are interested in. Whenever possible, it's best to follow the modelling diagram.

Since the tank was completely filled up at each petrol stop, the petrol bought at each stop corresponds to the petrol used since the previous stop. Thus, you can calculate the petrol consumption between 18.01.10 and 18.02.10 using the data in Table 2. This is done in Example 8.

Example 8   *Petrol consumption*

From Table 2, there were 44.98 litres needed to fill up the tank on 18.02.10. This corresponds to the amount of petrol used since the previous fill on 18.01.10.

Next, we need to convert 44.98 litres into gallons. Now, 1 gallon equals 4.546 09 litres, hence

44.98 litres $= 44.98/4.546\,09$ gallons $= 9.894\,216\,788$ gallons.

Remembering to keep maximum accuracy in intermediate calculations, we keep this ridiculously long number provided by a calculator for the time being in order to calculate the miles per gallon. From Activity 8, the car travelled 266 miles, so the fuel consumption in miles per gallon is

$266/9.894\,216\,788 = 26.884\,391\,73$.

1. Pose

3. Analyse

Clearly, the eight decimal places give spurious accuracy to the result. But how should this number be rounded? In fact, there is a rule of thumb to guide this choice (discussed straight after this example) – and this rule indicates that the best choice here is to keep just one decimal place. Thus, our answer is that the car did an average of 26.9 miles per gallon between 18.01.10 and 18.02.10.

In Example 8, numbers obtained in the intermediate calculations contained a large number of decimal places. What degree of accuracy should be kept in the final result, to avoid quoting the final result with spurious accuracy? The answer depends on the numbers of **significant figures** involved.

The first significant figure of an unrounded number is its first non-zero digit, counting from the left. The next significant figure is the next digit (zero or other), and so on. Thus, for example, the third significant figure of the number 004 637 is 3; the fourth significant figure of the number 0.028 901 72 is 0. Rounding to a given number of significant figures is done just as before: for example, 004 637 rounded to two significant figures is 004 600 (or just 4600), 0.028 901 72 rounded to three significant figures is 0.0289.

After a number has been rounded, it may not be possible to say how many figures are significant, unless you are told how it was rounded. For example, take the number 004 637 rounded to two significant figures, which is 4600. The two significant figures are 4 and 6, and the last two zeros are not significant figures (that is, they are zeros because the number has been rounded). But 4600 is also what you would get by rounding 4601 to three significant figures, in which case the three significant figures are 4, 6 and 0. Or 4600 is what you would get by rounding 4600.1 to four significant figures, in which case the four significant figures are 4, 6, 0 and 0. Thus, a zero to the right of a rounded number may or may not be significant, according to how the rounding was done. However, when you see a measured quantity such as 4600 with no information about whether or how the number has been rounded, it is usually assumed that any zeros at the end are not significant.

Note that it's unlikely you'll ever encounter a number such as 004 637!

Activity 9 *Significant figures*

(a) How many significant figures are there in 2460 if it has been rounded to the nearest ten?

(b) How many significant figures are there in 0.003 610 if it has been rounded to six decimal places?

(c) How many significant figures are there in 910 if you are not told whether, or how, the number has been rounded? (Give two options.)

(d) Round the numbers 208.3 and 0.098 3765 to three significant figures.

After this digression on significant figures, we return to the problem of how to round the result of an arithmetic calculation. The following rule of thumb provides a rough guide to this.

A useful rule of thumb

The rule is not infallible and sometimes the last digit can be wrong even if you know precisely how the numbers have been rounded, but it is a useful general guide!

The 'output' result of a multiplication or division of several 'input' quantities, some of which have been rounded, should be rounded so that it has the same number of significant figures as the rounded input quantity with the *smallest* number of significant figures.

Note that only the *rounded* inputs come into this. For example, to obtain a percentage, you need to multiply by 100: this 100 is not a rounded number, so does not count when working out how many significant figures to keep. If you do not know whether a number has been rounded, then assume it has.

Example 9   *Rounding the petrol consumption*

The numbers involved in the calculation for Example 8 were: the distance, 266 miles, which has three significant figures; the conversion factor from litres to gallons, 4.54609, which has six significant figures; and the amount of petrol used, 44.98 litres, which has four significant figures. It is reasonable to regard all these numbers as having been rounded. So the rounded number with the least significant figures is distance, with three.

Thus, according to the rule of thumb, you should keep three significant figures in the final result. In Example 8 this was 26.884 391 73, so keeping three significant figures gives 26.9 miles per gallon. (Ignore the decimal place when counting the number of significant figures.)

In the following activity, have a go at calculating the petrol consumption, in miles per gallon, between the next two petrol stops in Table 2.

Activity 10   *Petrol consumption again*

Calculate the petrol consumption in miles per gallon between 18.02.10 and 04.03.10, rounding your final answer to the correct number of significant figures. (Use the conversion factor of 1 gallon = 4.546 09 litres.)

Whenever possible, it is better to do the whole calculation on your calculator without copying down intermediate numbers. This avoids making an error when copying, which is very easy to do. For example, in Activity 10, a suitable key sequence (provided your calculator has brackets) would be:

$$(112\,954 - 112\,616) \div (43.49 \div 4.546\,09) =$$

We can now proceed, by the method used in the solution to Activity 10, to calculate all the values of the petrol consumption between consecutive stops, using the data in Table 2. The results are presented in the last column of Table 3 – the answers have all been rounded to one decimal place. Also shown are the 'Period no.', where period 1 corresponds to the period between stops 1 and 2, period 2 to the period between stops 2 and 3, and so on, and the mileages at the petrol stops at the start ('Mileage reading 1') and end ('Mileage reading 2') of each period.

The buttons on your calculator may be labelled differently; this is just one possible sequence: there are others.

Table 3 Petrol consumption results 2010–2012

Period no.	Mileage reading 1	Mileage reading 2	Distance (miles)	Petrol used (gallons)	Expenditure (£)	Consumption (miles per gallon)
1	112 350	112 616	266	9.89	49.89	26.9
2	112 616	112 954	338	9.57	48.67	35.3
3	112 954	113 269	315	9.93	52.31	31.7
4	113 269	113 564	295	9.19	50.07	32.1
5	113 564	113 857	293	9.73	53.06	30.1
6	113 857	114 123	266	8.95	47.58	29.7
7	114 123	114 469	346	9.54	52.01	36.3
8	114 469	114 823	354	9.15	48.21	38.7
9	114 823	115 091	268	9.06	46.48	29.6
10	115 091	115 360	269	10.08	51.75	26.7
11	115 360	115 706	346	9.49	49.57	36.5
12	115 706	115 984	278	9.74	51.30	28.6
13	115 984	116 202	218	8.35	44.37	26.1
14	116 202	116 542	340	9.96	54.31	34.1
15	116 542	116 795	253	8.99	49.84	28.1
16	116 795	117 071	276	8.25	47.58	33.5
17	117 071	117 417	346	9.87	56.97	35.0
18	117 417	117 736	319	8.93	51.52	35.7
19	117 736	118 030	294	7.26	41.90	40.5
20	118 030	118 368	338	9.43	55.69	35.8
21	118 368	118 748	380	10.44	60.25	36.4
22	118 748	119 064	316	8.08	47.70	39.1
23	119 064	119 419	355	9.14	54.42	38.8
24	119 419	119 773	354	10.02	60.51	35.3
25	119 773	120 134	361	9.62	59.02	37.5
26	120 134	120 481	347	8.25	50.23	42.1
27	120 481	120 794	313	8.88	54.06	35.2
28	120 794	121 146	352	9.23	55.78	38.1
29	121 146	121 476	330	8.99	55.12	36.7
30	121 476	121 793	317	8.75	52.88	36.2
31	121 793	122 128	335	9.51	57.43	35.2
32	122 128	122 436	308	8.55	51.27	36.0
33	122 436	122 786	350	8.90	52.08	39.3
34	122 786	123 108	322	9.89	58.87	32.6

Note that the 'Petrol used' column in Table 3 has been expressed in gallons, and rounded to two decimal places. This column is included as an interesting intermediate result. However, the final petrol consumption figures were calculated using the unrounded values from Table 2.

In this section, we have seen that data always need to be carefully inspected and should be cleaned where necessary. Also, you have learned the technique of rounding. In the next section, we shall look at the values we have found for petrol consumption and try to display them in a way which may help us to see if there is any pattern in the data.

Exercises on Section 3

Exercise 3   *Round and round again*

Round 502.561 5297 to:

(a) six significant figures

(b) five decimal places

(c) the nearest whole number

(d) the nearest ten.

Exercise 4   *The population of the world*

In Activity 5, the population of the world was said to be 6 985 119 415 on 1 January 2012. Round this as follows, stating the number of significant figures in each case:

(a) the nearest ten thousand

(b) the nearest hundred thousand.

Exercise 5   *Litres per hundred kilometres*

In several countries, petrol consumption is calculated in litres per hundred kilometres. Using this measure and the data in Table 2, obtain the fuel consumption between stops 1 and 2. Take care to round the final result appropriately. Use the conversion factor of 1 mile = 1.609 344 kilometres.

4 Pictures of data

We are now ready to look for patterns in the petrol consumption data introduced in Section 3. One way of finding these patterns is to represent the data pictorially in some way and then to look at the picture. In this section we introduce one method of picturing data: the stemplot. Before jumping in and discussing the stemplot, however, let us see if we can discern any pattern at all from the only type of display which we have used so far on our petrol consumption data, namely, the table.

Let us extract the petrol consumption data from Table 3, referring each value to the period of time to which the value applies. For ease of reference, the data we need are laid out in Table 4.

Table 4   Petrol consumption 2010–2012: 1996 Honda Civic 1.4i

Period no.	Petrol consumption (miles per gallon)	Period no.	Petrol consumption (miles per gallon)
1	26.9	18	35.7
2	35.3	19	40.5
3	31.7	20	35.8
4	32.1	21	36.4
5	30.1	22	39.1
6	29.7	23	38.8
7	36.3	24	35.3
8	38.7	25	37.5
9	29.6	26	42.1
10	26.7	27	35.2
11	36.5	28	38.1
12	28.6	29	36.7
13	26.1	30	36.2
14	34.1	31	35.2
15	28.1	32	36.0
16	33.5	33	39.3
17	35.0	34	32.6

Does inspection of the 'Petrol consumption' columns of Table 4 as they stand give a clear impression of any aspects of the petrol consumption figures themselves? Apart from showing that most values are in the 'thirties' and a few are in the 'upper twenties' or 'early forties', it is not clear that they do. Can we do anything 'quick and easy' with the data which might reveal a pattern? Well, if we arrange the petrol consumption values in ascending order, for instance, then we obtain the order shown in Table 5, which should be read from left to right in successive rows.

Table 5   Petrol consumption values arranged in ascending order

26.1	26.7	26.9	28.1	28.6	29.6	29.7	30.1	31.7	32.1	32.6	33.5
34.1	35.0	35.2	35.2	35.3	35.3	35.7	35.8	36.0	36.2	36.3	36.4
36.5	36.7	37.5	38.1	38.7	38.8	39.1	39.3	40.5	42.1		

From Table 5, we can immediately see that there is no value below 26.1, seven values '35 point something', nothing above 42.1, etc.

What we would like is a way to display the sort of information that's shown in Table 5 directly in pictorial form. That is what the stemplot gives us.

4.1 Stemplots

The **stemplot** is a device for displaying numerical data in a pictorial structure. Our first example of a stemplot is shown in Figure 14, where we have plotted all the ordered petrol consumption data taken from Table 5.

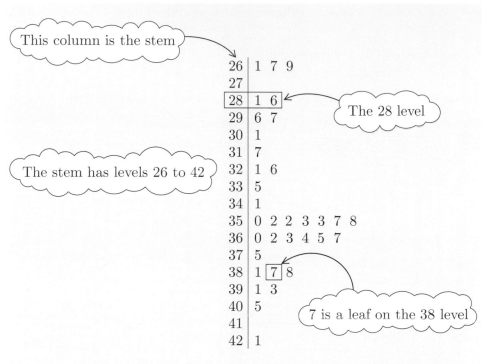

$$n = 34 \quad 26 \mid 1 \text{ represents } 26.1 \text{ miles per gallon}$$

Figure 14   Stemplot of the petrol consumption data

Stemplots are also called *stem-and-leaf* plots.

The three basic elements in the stemplot are the **stem**, the **levels** and the **leaves**. The **stem of a stemplot** is the single column of figures lying to the left of the vertical line, arranged vertically downwards in increasing order. In Figure 14, this consists of all the whole numbers from 26 to 42 inclusive. We do not need any numbers less than 26 because the lowest data value (26.1) lies between 26 and 27. Similarly, we do not need any numbers greater than 42 because the highest data value (42.1) lies between 42 and 43.

Corresponding to each number on the stem is a **level** of the stemplot, which is named after that number. The level actually consists of everything occurring 'on the same horizontal line' of the stemplot as the number used to name it. The '28 level' is surrounded by a box in Figure 14. Starting at the left-hand end of that box and moving to the right, we have first the number used to name the level (28), then a bit of the vertical line (which is used to keep the stem and leaves apart from one another) and finally two *separate* single digit numbers (1 and 6), each of which is referred to as a **leaf** of the stemplot. Each leaf on the stemplot corresponds to a single data value and the digit, from 0 to 9, used to represent it is derived from the data value itself. For example, the digit '7' on the '38 level', surrounded by a box in Figure 14, is a leaf on the '38 level' that represents the data value 38.7.

At the bottom of the stemplot are two pieces of information:

- The statement '$n = 34$', which indicates that there are 34 data values in the batch. Throughout this module we shall use the symbol n for the number of values in the batch, the **batch size**.

- '26 | 1 represents 26.1 miles per gallon', which is the rule (or key) enabling you to translate the combination of the level name (26) and leaf digit (1) into a data value as indicated above. This rule generally varies for different stemplots. It gives information about the units in which the data values are measured.

The next activity will give you some practice at reading a stemplot.

Japanese train timetables

Reading stemplots will come in handy if you go to Japan, where they are commonly used to represent train timetables, as in Figure 15.

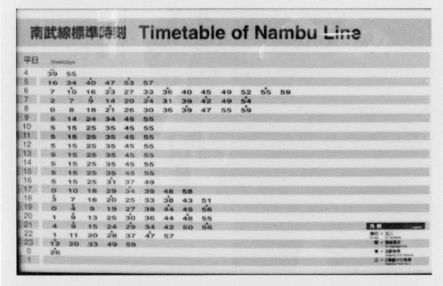

Figure 15   Train timetable for the Nambu Line, Japan

Activity 11   *Reading a stemplot*

Use the stemplot in Figure 14 to answer the following questions.

(a) How many levels does the stemplot have?

(b) Levels 27 and 41 have no leaves. What does this mean?

(c) How many levels have just a single leaf?

(d) How often did the value 35.3 occur in this batch? How is this represented on the stemplot?

One important thing to note about stemplots is that repeated values in the batch are represented by repeating the leaves. In Figure 14 the leaf 2 occurs twice at level 35, representing the value 35.2 occurring twice.

Another important feature is that, at each level, the leaf digits are *ordered*, increasing as you move away from the stem. This means that the data values are represented in order of *increasing* size as you move away from the stem at any particular level. As we shall see later, this is important when we want to determine certain things from a stemplot.

In Section 6 you will learn how to obtain stemplots using a computer.

In obtaining a stemplot by hand for a batch of data which has not been arranged in order of increasing size, as ours has been in Table 5, it is easiest initially to go through the data values one by one and draw up a stemplot by putting the leaves on each level in the order in which they actually occur. For example, if we had used the unordered values from Table 4 rather than the ordered values from Table 5, the initial *unordered stemplot* would have looked like Figure 16.

```
26 | 9 7 1
27 |
28 | 6 1
29 | 7 6
30 | 1
31 | 7
32 | 1 6
33 | 5
34 | 1
35 | 3 0 7 8 3 2 2
36 | 3 5 4 7 2 0
37 | 5
38 | 7 8 1
39 | 1 3
40 | 5
41 |
42 | 1
```

$n = 34$ 26 | 9 represents 26.9 miles per gallon

Figure 16   Unordered stemplot of the petrol consumption data

As a final step, the leaves on each level must be arranged in numerical order. For the petrol consumption data, Figure 14 would have resulted at this stage. The next activity will give you some practice at constructing a stemplot.

You have now covered the material related to Screencast 3 for Unit 1 (see the M140 website).

Activity 12   *Counting moths*

An ultraviolet moth-trap (as in Figure 17) was run at a location in North Buckinghamshire during many nights one September and the number of moths caught each night was counted. These nightly counts are given in Table 6 below.

Table 6   Nightly moth counts

| 47 | 21 | 16 | 39 | 24 | 34 | 21 | 34 | 49 | 20 | 37 | 65 |
| 67 | 21 | 37 | 46 | 29 | 41 | 47 | 24 | 22 | 19 | 54 | 71 |

Prepare a stemplot of these data, using the following steps.

(a) Explain why it suffices to use levels 1 to 7. Draw a vertical line, and write the numbers 1 to 7 as a column to the left of the line.

Figure 17   Trapping moths using ultraviolet light

(b) Work along the first row of data and then along the second row, writing down each leaf at the appropriate level to the right of the vertical line. So, for example, for the value 47, write the leaf 7 at the 4th level. Once you have done this for all the values in the table, you will have constructed the unordered stemplot.

(c) Prepare a second stemplot with the leaves in correct numerical order.

(d) Label the stemplot in part (c) with the batch size and the rule to interpret each stem and leaf.

The following box summarises the key features of a stemplot.

> **The key features of a stemplot**
>
> - A stemplot breaks up the range of data values into a column (stem) of ordered levels corresponding to convenient equal intervals.
>
> - The levels of a stemplot are labelled so that we know what each interval is.
>
> - A stemplot represents data values in order within each interval (level) using single digit leaves.
>
> Each leaf of a stemplot represents a data value whose first few significant figures are the level followed by the value for the leaf. For example, leaf b at level a represents a data value for which the significant figures start 'ab'.

So what does the stemplot actually give us which we did not have before? This is the topic of the next example.

Example 10   *Interpreting the petrol consumption stemplot*

The stemplot in Figure 14 provides a useful 'picture' of the data from which several features are apparent. For a start, the maximum and minimum values are easily read off from the plot (42.1 and 26.1 respectively).

4. Interpret

Also, you could say that there is a 'pattern' and perhaps describe it as 'an obvious clustering around the 35 and 36 levels which diminishes gradually towards higher values and more steeply towards lower values, with perhaps a smaller clustering arising around the 26 to 29 levels'. This type of qualitative statement can often be made directly after simply *looking* at a stemplot. This would be much more difficult to do by staring at a table of data values, even an ordered one!

This pattern can begin to suggest possible interpretations of the data. Typically, the fuel consumption lies around the mid to high thirties (miles per gallon), but occasionally there are periods of higher petrol consumption, with values around the mid to high twenties.

The interpretation of the stemplot in Example 10 was based on the following key factors, which help to describe what is usually called the 'distribution' of the data.

These matters will be discussed more fully in Section 5.

> **Interpreting a stemplot**
>
> The *number* of leaves at each level tells us the number of data values in each interval. This indicates if there are any 'gaps' without many values, and where the maximum and minimum values are.
>
> *Comparing* the numbers of leaves at the various levels indicates whether the data values 'cluster together' in particular regions.

The next activity will give you some practice at interpreting a stemplot.

Activity 13   *Interpreting the moth-counts stemplot*

In Activity 12, you prepared a stemplot for the data in Table 6. Comment on two aspects of the data revealed by your stemplot.

4.2 The median and the range

One reason for ordering the data on a stemplot is that it helps to find the **middle** of the batch. This is illustrated in the following example.

Example 11   *The middle of the petrol consumption data*

The petrol consumption data in Figure 14 show that the data values lie between levels 26 and 42, but cluster around the levels 35 and 36. Suppose now that we want to answer the question:

> *How many miles per gallon does the car do?*

To answer this we should try and find a *single* number which is representative of the whole batch. The middle value of the data seems like it ought to be a good one to use (because it's in the middle!).

If we had an *odd* number n of data values, like 21 say, there would be only *one* middle value, which in that case would be the 11th value, taken from either end of the ordered data. There would be 10 values on each side.

However, in Figure 14 we see that $n = 34$, which is even. In this case there are *two* middle values, the 17th and 18th. Because there is no way to choose between them, we take the representative value to be half the sum

The word *median* comes from the Latin word for middle.

(i.e. the average) of these two middle values. The quantity we define in this way is called the **median**.

If we look at Figure 14 and start counting leaves at the lowest value (that is, from the top of the stemplot), then the 17th data value is 35.3 and the 18th data value is also 35.3. So the median for the petrol consumption data is $(35.3 + 35.3)/2 = 35.3$, in miles per gallon. It so happens in this case that the median has a single decimal place, the same level of accuracy as is found in the data; in other situations the level of accuracy might not be the same, in which case the median would be rounded to match the rest of the data.

The median is an important quantity in statistics, which merits its own special box.

The median

The median of a batch of data is the middle of the ordered batch.

- If the batch size is odd,

    median = middle data value.

- If the batch size is even,

    median = average of the two middle data values

    $$= \frac{\text{sum of the two middle data values}}{2}.$$

The median should be rounded to the same level of accuracy as the original data.

We round the median to the same level of accuracy as the original data so as to avoid introducing any spurious accuracy. The median of a batch will often be used in this module as a single representative figure for a batch of data. It provides a measurement of the typical value or **location** of the batch.

Activity 14   *The median moth count*

Use the ordered stemplot you obtained in Activity 12 to find the median of the moth-trap data.

Note that if the batch size is even, the median can take a value that is not equal to *any* of the data values in the batch – this happened for the moth-trap data in Activity 14.

One of the big advantages of the median is that it is not affected by unusually large or small observations in a batch of data. Such extreme observations are by their very nature not typical, and so it is desirable that they should not affect our measure of what is a 'typical' value. This issue is illustrated in the next example.

Example 12   *Average salaries for high-paid occupations*

The Annual Survey of Hours and Earnings (ASHE) is undertaken annually by the Office of National Statistics and records the occupations and pay for a 1% sample of employees in the UK. The survey does not cover self-employed people and does not take into account non-salary rewards such as bonuses and share options. Thus it does not provide a full picture of income inequality in the UK (Figure 18). Table 7 shows the median annual salaries for the top 20 highest-paid categories of employees, derived from the 2011 ASHE data by a national newspaper. For example, the top category represents 'Heads of major organisations', and the value £114 550 represents the median salary among all employees surveyed who were in that category.

Figure 18   Income inequality provides a focus for political protest especially at times of economic crisis, as with the 2011 'Occupy' movement pictured here

Table 7   Median salaries for the 20 highest-paid occupations in 2011

44 160	44 870	45 260	45 360	45 410	45 420	47 250	47 900	48 450	51 090
52 900	53 740	56 800	58 750	59 300	60 100	74 440	78 180	82 960	114 550

Suppose now that we wish to represent these data using a stemplot with levels 4 to 11. To represent the data on a stemplot, we retain one leaf digit, and thus drop the last three digits of each number. Numbers for which the last digits have been dropped without rounding are said to have been **truncated**. Thus, 44 160 and 44 870 are both truncated to 44. The stemplot based on the truncated data is shown in Figure 19. (It is customary, when drawing a stemplot, *not* to round the values. This makes it easier to vary how the stem is chosen.)

```
 4 | 4 4 5 5 5 5 7 7 8
 5 | 1 2 3 6 8 9
 6 | 0
 7 | 4 8
 8 | 2
 9 |
10 |
11 | 4
```

$n = 20$ 4 | 4 represents £44 000

Figure 19   Stemplot of median salaries for highest-paid occupations

The single value '11 | 4', representing £114 000, is noticeably separated from the rest of the data. Such a value is called an **outlier**. (Precisely how far away from the main body of data an entry has to be before it can be deemed to be an outlier is somewhat arbitrary.)

Since there are 20 data points, the median is the average of the 10th and 11th largest values. From the stemplot, these are £51 000 and £52 000, so the median (calculated from the stemplot) is £51 500; rounding this to the same accuracy as the rest of the data on the stemplot gives £52 000.

The original values are £51 090 and £52 900, so the median calculated from the data is £51 995. Rounding this value to the same level of accuracy as the data (which appears to be given to the nearest £10) gives £52 000, the same as the median calculated from the stemplot. However, generally, the median calculated from the data and from the stemplot may not coincide exactly, due to the truncation of the data to construct the stemplot.

Note that the high value of the outlier does not influence the calculation of the median. You would obtain the same result if all heads of major organisations were paid millions (which, of course, some are). Similarly, the result is not influenced by the lowest value in the dataset. The median is said to be **resistant** to outliers.

To make a stemplot more compact, outliers are often listed separately, as in Figure 20 for the median salary data.

```
4 | 4 4 5 5 5 5 7 7 8
5 | 1 2 3 6 8 9
6 | 0
7 | 4 8
8 | 2
────────────────
HI    114
```

$$n = 20 \quad 4 \mid 4 \text{ represents } £44\,000$$

Figure 20   Representing outliers on a stemplot

If there are several outliers, they are listed in order of size. Note that the notation used for them is 'level number followed by leaf digit'. For instance, in Figure 20, 114 represents £114 000. The label *HI* indicates that this outlier is a **high outlier**; that is, that its value is significantly *greater* than the values in the main body of the stemplot. High outliers are always listed *below* the stem, in increasing order.

Low outliers are values of the data that are significantly *less* than the values in the main body of the stemplot. The low outliers are always listed *above* the stem, in increasing order, and are labelled *LO*. (There are no low outliers in Figure 20.)

Activity 15   *Low salaries*

The ASHE (see Example 12) also collected information on part-time and low-paid jobs. Table 8 gives the median annual salary paid for the twenty lowest-paid occupations in 2011. (Many of these involve primarily part-time work.) The two lowest values correspond to school midday assistants and school crossing patrol attendants.

Table 8   Median salaries for the 20 lowest-paid occupations in 2011

2 190	3 630	5 530	5 660	6 060	6 500	6 620	6 680	6 980	7 030
7 870	8 330	8 360	8 480	8 740	8 840	9 120	9 600	9 900	9 980

(a)   Construct a stemplot for the data in Table 8 with levels 2 to 9 (i.e. truncate the data after the second digit, without rounding). Treat the two lowest values as outliers and list them separately.

(b)   Calculate the median for these data from the stemplot.

(c)   Would the median change if the two lowest-paid occupations each had a rise of £1000? Explain your answer.

Another important property of a batch of data, which certainly strikes you straight away when you look at a stemplot, is its **spread**, or **scatter**. The stemplot gives a good *picture* of the spread but it would be convenient to have a single *number* which represents it, in the way the median represents the overall location of the values in a batch. Such numbers are called **measures of spread**. The simplest single-figure summary of the spread is the distance between the two extreme values, that is, the distance between the maximum and minimum. This is called the **range**.

The range

The range of a batch is the distance between the two extreme values. It can be calculated from the formula:

$$\text{range} = E_U - E_L,$$

where E_U is the **upper extreme** (the largest value, or maximum) and E_L is the **lower extreme** (the smallest value, or minimum).

Example 13   *Calculating the range*

The range of the batch of petrol consumption data in Figure 14 is calculated from the two extreme values, which are:

$$E_U = 42.1 \quad \text{and} \quad E_L = 26.1.$$

Therefore the range, in miles per gallon, is:

$$E_U - E_L = 42.1 - 26.1 = 16.0.$$

Note that there is no need to round the value, as subtracting (or adding) values does not increase the number of decimal places. However, also note that the result is reported as 16.0 rather than 16, to indicate that the result is accurate to the nearest 0.1 miles per gallon (and so has three significant figures).

Activity 16   *The range of top salaries*

Calculate the range of the batch of median salaries for the 20 highest-paid occupations in the stemplot of Figure 19.

As with the median, the range can be calculated directly from the original data, rather than from the stemplot. Because the range depends only upon the extreme values, it is very easy to calculate.

However, unlike the median, the range is not resistant to outliers. It is quite possible for a batch of data to have most of its data values clustered in quite a narrow region, but to have, say, a single high outlier and a single low outlier, both very far from all the other values. Then, as the two extreme values are far from the rest of the data, the distance between them gives little information about how tightly clustered all the rest of the data values are. The same situation often applies even if only one of the extreme values is an outlier. Units 2 and 3 introduce better measures of spread.

In this section, the concept of a stemplot has been introduced. You have seen how it can be used to calculate the median and we have looked briefly at how to interpret a stemplot to describe the distribution of the batch of data. In the next section, you will learn how to extract more information from a stemplot about one aspect of the distribution of a batch of data – its shape.

Exercises on Section 4

Table 9 gives the shot-put results for 15 senior male athletes in a UK athletics championship, in June 2011. The athletes were grouped into two pools, A and B. The results are in metres.

Table 9   Shot-put championship results (metres)

| Pool A | 12.57 | 12.75 | 15.43 | 16.27 | 16.40 | 16.70 | 18.05 | |
| Pool B | 11.98 | 12.37 | 13.87 | 13.91 | 14.38 | 15.10 | 15.28 | 16.47 |

(Data source: UK Athletics)

(a) Construct a stemplot for all 15 values with levels 11 to 18.

(b) Calculate the median from the stemplot.

(c) Obtain the extreme values and the range from the stemplot.

(d) Briefly comment on the distribution of this batch of data. Are there any potential outliers?

Exercise 7   *Wooden toy prices*

Table 10 shows the prices, in increasing order, of 28 different wooden toys costing under £20 listed by an online retailer in February 2012.

Table 10   Wooden toy prices (£)

1.21	1.21	4.05	5.99	6.04	7.25	7.50
7.99	7.99	8.49	8.75	9.10	9.40	9.43
9.50	9.99	10.00	10.18	10.38	10.95	11.16
11.95	11.99	12.75	13.18	13.49	14.15	17.21

(a) Construct a stemplot for these data, with levels 1 to 17. Identify three outliers on the stemplot.

(b) Construct a second stemplot for these data, with the outliers listed separately.

(c) Calculate the median from the stemplot in part (b).

(d) Obtain the extreme values and the range from the stemplot in part (b).

(e) Briefly comment on the distribution of this batch of data.

5 The shape of a batch

The stemplot is a very good method of picturing a batch of data because it enables you to see each individual data value (though these may be truncated) and, at the same time, to see the batch as a whole. It also shows the data values in numerical order, so you can easily find the 'middle' value (the median) and also the largest and smallest values (the upper and lower extremes). Perhaps its greatest strength, however, is that it shows you whether the values are spread out evenly or clustered together, and where this clustering takes place if so.

So a stemplot contains, in a readily accessible form, a lot of information about the *shape* of the values in a batch. Later in this section we shall look at ways of summarising such information. First, however, we shall look in more detail at how to prepare a useful stemplot of a batch of data, because this is frequently not as straightforward as it may have seemed so far.

5.1   How many levels?

In the stemplots you have drawn so far we have always told you the levels to put on the stem. Getting the number of levels right is important, since otherwise you may not get a useful impression of the overall shape of the batch. This is illustrated by the next example.

Example 14   *Stemplots that are spread out or squashed up*

The mileage readings, rounded to the nearest hundred miles, are collected for 22 cars on sale at a used car lot. The lowest mileage is 23 300 miles and the highest is 45 000 miles. If the stemplot is drawn with levels 23 to 45, so that each level represents 1000 miles, this gives the stemplot in Figure 21.

```
23 | 3
24 |
25 | 2
26 | 4  6
27 | 1  9
28 | 4
29 |
30 | 8
31 | 2  7  9
32 | 3
33 | 0
34 | 5
35 | 2
36 | 8  9
37 |
38 | 2
39 | 4
40 |
41 | 3
42 |
43 | 6
44 |
45 | 0
```

$n = 22$ 23 | 3 represents 23 300 miles

Figure 21   Stemplot of mileage of used cars (too many levels)

The values on the stemplot in Figure 21 are very spread out, which makes it difficult to get a good impression of the shape of the batch. The problem is that there are too many levels – there are 23 levels for 22 data values! So, the number of levels needs to be reduced in some way. Reducing them so that the levels are separated by 10 000 rather than 1000 miles produces the stemplot in Figure 22.

```
2 | 3  5  6  6  7  7  8
3 | 0  1  1  1  2  3  4  5  6  6  8  9
4 | 1  3  5
```

$n = 22$ 2 | 3 represents 23 000 miles

Figure 22   Stemplot of mileage of used cars (too few levels)

Now the stemplot is far too squashed up, so that, again, nothing much can be said about the shape of the batch. Reducing the number of levels from 23 to three is too drastic.

Minitab will be introduced in Section 6

Choosing a suitable number of levels in a stemplot is a matter of trial and error. In this unit, we will always either tell you what levels to put on the stem of a stemplot, or let Minitab (a statistical package) do the work. However, there is one particular technique that you need to know: how to stretch a stemplot.

Example 15   *Stretched stemplots*

We want a way of stretching our squashed-up stemplot in Figure 22, by increasing the number of levels (without having too many). The idea of the **stretched stemplot** is to split each level into two or more parts. Thus, for instance, level 2, which currently can sprout leaves 0–9, is split into two parts, one bearing leaves 0–4 and one bearing leaves 5–9. Therefore, our stemplot with levels 2, 3 and 4 could now be stretched so as to have the following structure.

$$
\begin{array}{c|l}
2 & \text{leaves } 0\text{--}4 \\
2 & \text{leaves } 5\text{--}9 \\
3 & \text{leaves } 0\text{--}4 \\
3 & \text{leaves } 5\text{--}9 \\
4 & \text{leaves } 0\text{--}4 \\
4 & \text{leaves } 5\text{--}9 \\
\end{array}
$$

For example, level 3 of the stemplot in Figure 22 splits into two parts.

$$
\begin{array}{c|ccccccc}
3 & 0 & 1 & 1 & 1 & 2 & 3 & 4 \\
3 & 5 & 6 & 6 & 8 & 9 \\
\end{array}
$$

Splitting all the levels in this way gives the stretched stemplot in Figure 23, which now has six levels (or parts of levels).

$$
\begin{array}{c|ccccccc}
2 & 3 \\
2 & 5 & 6 & 6 & 7 & 7 & 8 \\
3 & 0 & 1 & 1 & 1 & 2 & 3 & 4 \\
3 & 5 & 6 & 6 & 8 & 9 \\
4 & 1 & 3 \\
4 & 5 \\
\end{array}
$$

$n = 22$ $2 \mid 3$ represents 23 000 miles

Figure 23   Stretched stemplot of mileages of used cars

This is certainly an improvement over Figure 22, although it is rather squashed still, with little detail in the middle. Can we do better? Well, we can try – by stretching the stemplot a bit more and splitting each level into five rather than two parts, each with just two leaves. The stemplot will now have the following structure, with up to 15 parts.

```
2 | leaves 0–1
2 | leaves 2–3
2 | leaves 4–5
2 | leaves 6–7
2 | leaves 8–9
3 | leaves 0–1
3 | leaves 2–3
3 | leaves 4–5
3 | leaves 6–7
3 | leaves 8–9
4 | leaves 0–1
4 | leaves 2–3
4 | leaves 4–5
4 | leaves 6–7
4 | leaves 8–9
```

For example, level 3 of the stemplot in Figure 22 now splits into five parts.

```
3 | 0 1 1 1
3 | 2 3
3 | 4 5
3 | 6 6
3 | 8 9
```

Splitting all the levels in this way gives the stretched stemplot in Figure 24, which has 12 levels (or parts of levels).

```
2 | 3
2 | 5
2 | 6 6 7 7
2 | 8
3 | 0 1 1 1
3 | 2 3
3 | 4 5
3 | 6 6
3 | 8 9
4 | 1
4 | 3
4 | 5
```

$n = 22$ $2 \mid 3$ represents $23\,000$ miles

Figure 24   Another stretched stemplot of mileages of used cars

This gives a further, possibly better, representation of the shape of the batch. The values are quite evenly spread between 25 000 and 40 000 miles, with some clustering between 25 000 and 31 000 miles.

Example 15 is the subject of Screencast 4 for Unit 1 (see the M140 website).

Stretching stemplots gives you greater flexibility to choose the right number of levels for your data. The following activity will give you some practice at doing this.

Activity 17   *Price of digital televisions*

The following are the prices of 26 digital televisions with 22- to 26-inch LED screens, quoted online by a large department store in February 2012. The prices have been rounded to the nearest pound, to eliminate the distraction of having to deal with many prices ending in 9.99.

Table 11   Prices of digital televisions (£)

170	180	190	200	220	229	230	230	230
230	250	269	269	270	279	299	300	300
315	320	349	350	400	429	649	699	

(a) Construct a stemplot with levels 1, 2, 3 and 4, with the two high outliers listed separately.

(b) Stretch the stemplot you obtained in part (a) so that each level is split into two parts.

(c) Now stretch the stemplot you obtained in part (a) so that each level is split into five parts.

(d) Briefly comment on the different stemplots you have obtained.

Whether or not a squeezed or stretched stemplot is an improvement on the original stemplot is largely subjective. The aim is to obtain a stemplot which is easy to read, contains all the important information about the batch of data and reveals interesting or important patterns within it.

The next activity will give you some practice at obtaining a useful stemplot.

Activity 18   *Long-jump championship results*

Table 12 gives the results for 26 senior male athletes in a long-jump competition in the UK in June 2011. A long jump, pictured in Figure 25, is measured in metres.

Table 12   Long-jump championship results (metres)

| 6.53 | 6.44 | 7.38 | 4.36 | 6.99 | 4.68 | 6.96 | 5.60 | 6.72 | 6.24 | 7.15 | 6.41 | 6.64 |
| 6.81 | 6.05 | 6.73 | 5.92 | 6.45 | 6.37 | 6.94 | 6.26 | 6.59 | 6.35 | 6.52 | 6.36 | 6.93 |

(Data source: UK Athletics)

(a) Construct a stemplot of the data with levels 4 to 7.

(b) Stretch the stemplot you obtained in part (a) so that each level is split into two parts.

(c) Stretch the stemplot you obtained in part (a) so that each level is split into five parts, with two low outliers listed separately.

(d) Comment on the three stemplots you have obtained. Which stemplot do you think provides the most useful information?

Figure 25   Long jump athlete getting ready for landing

5.2   Peaks and symmetry

Once we have pictured a batch of data by preparing a stemplot, we can describe its **shape**. There are several things to look for, including the number of *peaks* and if there is any *symmetry* in the shape. (Figure 26 shows a symmetric 'peak'.)

Peaks

Batches of data are categorised according to the number of *clear* peaks they have. That is, levels (or parts of levels) that have more leaves than nearby levels (or parts of levels).

Figure 26   Mount Fuji, Japan

Example 16   *Identifying the peaks*

Figure 27 shows a stemplot of the moth counts discussed in Activity 12.

```
 1 | 6 9
 2 | 0 1 1 1 2 4 4 9
 3 | 4 4 7 7 9
 4 | 1 6 7 7 9
 5 | 4
 6 | 5 7
 7 | 1
```

$n = 24$ $1\,|\,6$ represents a count of 16

Figure 27   Stemplot of moth counts

The moth counts in this stemplot have one clear peak around level 2. Although level 6 has two leaves while levels 5 and 7 have only one leaf, this does not qualify level 6 as a clear peak. This is because even one extra leaf on level 5 would remove this peak. It's important not to over-interpret every small bump in the data as a peak, but to focus on the main features.

Sometimes the number of peaks is not so clear. For example, the wooden toy prices of Exercise 7 represented in the stemplot of Figure 28 (below) certainly cluster in the middle, around levels 7 to 10.

```
  1 | 2 2
  2 |
  3 |
  4 | 0
  5 | 9
  6 | 0
  7 | 2 5 9 9
  8 | 4 7
  9 | 1 4 4 5 9
 10 | 0 1 3 9
 11 | 1 9 9
 12 | 7
 13 | 1 4
 14 | 1
 15 |
 16 |
 17 | 2
```

$n = 28$ $1\,|\,2$ represents £1.20

Figure 28   Stemplot of wooden toy prices

There is a major peak at level 9 and perhaps a secondary peak at level 7, but no other clear peaks. The fact that levels 1 and 13 have two leaves is not worth mentioning, as small bumps in the data can occur by chance.

The statistical word for a peak is a **mode**. A batch with just one mode is called **unimodal**. Thus the first batch in Example 16 is clearly unimodal because it has just one peak. As mentioned above, we only count 'clear' peaks, and not small bumps which might be due to chance occurrences: it's important not to attach undue importance to such minor irregularities. However, as often is the case in statistics, what constitutes a 'clear' peak can be rather subjective!

Some data have more than one clear peak, as illustrated in the next example.

Example 17 *Wind turbines*

Data were collected on the power produced by a 100 kilowatt wind turbine, like that shown in Figure 29, during 44 periods of one hour each. It is usual to measure the output over an hour to smooth out fluctuations due to short severe gusts of wind. The stemplot of this batch of data is shown in Figure 30.

Figure 29 Wind turbines

```
 0 | 0 0 0 0 0 0 0 0 0 0 0 0 2 2 5 6 6 7 8
 1 | 5 6 6
 2 | 2
 3 | 3
 4 | 7
 5 | 6
 6 | 5 8
 7 | 0 1
 8 | 1 3
 9 | 2 8
10 | 1 2 2 3 4 4 5 5 6
```

$n = 44$ 10 | 6 represents 106 kilowatts

Figure 30 Stemplot of wind-turbine power output

You can see that there are a lot of readings for level 0 from when there was little or no wind, and so there is a mode at 0. The turbine is designed not to exceed its maximum output, so the distribution is cut off sharply. However, there are many occasions when the turbine is close to producing its maximum power output, and so there is a second mode at about 100 kilowatts. The batch has two modes as the data values are concentrated at each end.

Usually we have used the first number in the stemplot to explain the meaning of the stem and leaves. In Figure 30 we have used the last, 10 | 6, as 0 | 0 is not very helpful.

Example 17 presented data with two clear peaks. Such data are said to be **bimodal**. Data with three or more clear peaks are said to be **multimodal**. In the next activity you will have a go at identifying the number of peaks in a dataset.

Example 17 is the subject of Screencast 5 for Unit 1 (see the M140 website).

Activity 19   *Hunting the bumps*

How many modes are there in the following two datasets and how would you describe these data: unimodal, bimodal, or something else?

(a) Table 13 gives the coal production in the UK in 1970/71 in the 18 regions with coal-mines. Figure 31 is a stemplot of the regional coal production from Table 13.

Table 13   Coal production (thousand tonnes) by region, in UK coalmines 1970/71

Scottish North	5 283	North Western	6 132
Scottish South	5 892	North Derbyshire	9 777
Northumberland	6 272	North Nottingham	12 070
North Durham	5 111	South Nottingham	10 555
South Durham	7 551	South Midlands	8 859
North Yorkshire	9 481	Staffordshire	8 302
Doncaster	8 010	East Wales	6 899
Barnsley	7 794	West Wales	4 787
South Yorkshire	9 471	Kent	1 008

```
 1 | 0
 2 |
 3 |
 4 | 7
 5 | 1  2  8
 6 | 1  2  8
 7 | 5  7
 8 | 0  3  8
 9 | 4  4  7
10 | 5
11 |
12 | 0
```

$n = 18$ $1 \mid 0$ represents 1 000 000 tonnes

Figure 31   Stemplot of UK coal production, 1970/71

(b) Figure 32 is a stemplot of the times taken in the finals of 400-metre races in England in June 2011.

```
47 | 7 8
48 | 0 2 2 7 8 9
49 | 0 4 6 6
50 | 8
51 | 1
52 |
53 | 9
54 |
55 | 1 3
56 | 6 6
57 | 2 2 3 4 8
58 | 3 9 9
59 | 2 4
60 | 1 2
```

$n = 31$ 47 | 7 represents 47.7 seconds

Figure 32   Stemplot of times in 400-metre races

(Data source: UK Athletics)

Symmetry

If a horizontal line can be drawn across the stemplot of a batch so that the shape on one side is almost the mirror image of the shape on the other side then the batch is said to be **symmetric**.

Example 18 *Symmetric or not?*

Figure 33 shows the stemplot of percentage scores for 21 students in an English test.

```
0 | 5
1 | 2
2 | 9
3 | 1 3 7
4 | 0 1 4 6
─────────────────
5 | 2 6 7 9
6 | 4 8 9
7 | 1 7
8 | 6
9 | 3
```

$n = 21$ $0 \mid 5$ represents a score of 5%

Figure 33 Stemplot of percentage scores in an English test

The batch of data in Figure 33 is virtually symmetric about the line drawn between levels 4 and 5, which is as near as possible to the median, so about half the values lie each side of it. (The median of this dataset is 52%.) The symmetry of the stemplot is not quite perfect, as level 2 has only one leaf while level 7 has two leaves, but small differences between the two sides can occur by chance and so the batch should be regarded as symmetric.

This is the same as Figure 19.

On the other hand, consider the stemplot of median salaries for the 20 highest-paid occupations, in Figure 34.

```
 4 | 4 4 5 5 5 5 7 7 8
 5 | 1 2 3 6 8 9
 6 | 0
 7 | 4 8
 8 | 2
 9 |
10 |
11 | 4
```

$n = 20$ $4 \mid 4$ represents £44 000

Figure 34 Stemplot of median salaries for highest-paid occupations

This has a single peak at level 4, dropping down at higher salaries. The batch is clearly not symmetric.

A batch of data which is not symmetric is called **skew**.

A batch like that in Figure 34, where the large values are spread out and the small values are close together, is called **right-skew**. This name originates from another method of plotting data values, where the stemplot is effectively turned anticlockwise through a right angle, thus putting it on its side so that the small data values occur on the left and the large values on the right, as in Figure 35.

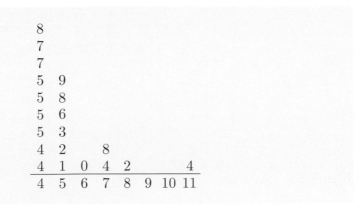

The seriously skew Leaning Tower of Pisa

Figure 35   The stemplot of Figure 34 turned on its side

An equivalent way of thinking about skewness involves the **tails of a batch**. A batch has two tails: the lower tail is the set of values up to and including the largest mode (that is, the highest peak), and the upper tail is the set of values from the largest mode up. In a symmetric batch, the two tails are of similar length, and in a skew batch, one tail is more spread out than the other. If the batch is right-skew, the spread-out tail lies numerically above the mode; in Figure 35, it is to the *right*.

Another possibility in a non-symmetric batch is that the large values are close together and the low values are spread out. Such a batch is called **left-skew** because the spread-out tail would be on the *left* if the stemplot were turned on its side as described above.

Right skewness is also often referred to as *positive skewness* and left skewness as *negative skewness*.

Activity 20   *Spotting the skew*

Decide whether the batches in the following stemplots are symmetric, right-skew or left-skew.

(a) The moth-trap data from Activity 12.

```
1 | 6 9
2 | 0 1 1 1 2 4 4 9
3 | 4 4 7 7 9
4 | 1 6 7 7 9
5 | 4
6 | 5 7
7 | 1
```

$n = 24$ $1 \mid 6$ represents a count of 16

Figure 36   Stemplot of moth counts

(b) Percentage scores in arithmetic obtained by 33 school students.

```
 0 | 7
 1 | 5
 2 |
 3 | 3 5
 4 | 2 2 3
 5 | 5 8
 6 | 4 6 8
 7 | 1 1 6 8 9
 8 | 0 1 1 3 4 5 5 6 9
 9 | 1 1 3 5 9
10 | 0 0
```

$n = 33$ $0 \mid 7$ represents a score of 7%

Figure 37   Stemplot of percentage scores in arithmetic

In this section, we have looked at ways of displaying and summarising a batch of data, so as to describe its shape in a useful manner. You have seen that it is important to choose the number of levels in a stemplot so that it is neither too spread out nor too cramped, and you have learned how to stretch a stemplot. You have also learned how to identify the modes of a batch of data and to say whether a batch is symmetric, right-skew or left-skew.

Exercises on Section 5

Exercise 8   *Women's triple jump*

Table 14 shows the performances of 16 senior female athletes in the triple jump during a UK championship in June 2011.

Table 14   Triple jump results (metres)

13.45	12.38	12.30	12.23	11.54	11.37	11.33	10.01
13.10	12.20	10.83	10.29	9.92	9.80	8.21	8.15

(Data source: UK Athletics)

(a) Construct a stemplot of these data with levels 8 to 13.

(b) Stretch the stemplot you obtained in part (a), by splitting each level into two parts.

(c) Comment briefly on the two stemplots. Identify two features of the data that are more apparent in the stretched stemplot.

Exercise 9   *Describing shapes*

For each of the two stemplots listed below, say how many modes there are, and describe the batch in terms of its symmetry or skew.

(a) The stemplot in Figure 38, showing the median salaries in the 20 lowest-paid occupations (discussed in Activity 15).

```
2 | 1
3 | 6
4 |
5 | 5 6
6 | 0 5 6 6 9
7 | 0 8
8 | 3 3 4 7 8
9 | 1 6 9 9
```

$n = 20$ $2 \,|\, 1$ represents £2100

Figure 38   Stemplot of median salaries for the 20 lowest-paid occupations

(b) The stemplot in Figure 39, displaying the results of the shot-put competition described in Exercise 6 at the end of Section 4.

$$
\begin{array}{r|l}
11 & 9 \\
12 & 3\ \ 5\ \ 7 \\
13 & 8\ \ 9 \\
14 & 3 \\
15 & 1\ \ 2\ \ 4 \\
16 & 2\ \ 4\ \ 4\ \ 7 \\
17 & \\
18 & 0 \\
\end{array}
$$

$n = 15$ $11 \mid 9$ represents 11.9 metres

Figure 39   Stemplot of the shot-put data

6 Computer work: introducing Minitab

In this section, the statistical package Minitab is introduced via the Computer Book. You will learn how to use Minitab, including how to:

- perform calculations on data
- obtain stemplots
- print output
- paste output into another document.

You should now turn to the Computer Book and work through the Introduction and Chapter 1.

7 Completing the assignments

There are two kinds of assignments in M140: interactive computer-marked assignments (iCMAs) and tutor-marked assignments (TMAs). The assignments and the instructions for submitting them are on the M140 website. This section provides some advice on how to complete these assignments, starting with some general advice on when to start working on them.

Most students find it best to start working on each assignment fairly soon after studying the material on which it is based. This usually means tackling the assignment soon after studying the unit. It is usually not a good idea to defer starting work on an assignment until close to the cut-off date. This is because you may need some time to revise some topics, or contact your tutor with questions, and you are unlikely to produce your best work if you are under time pressure. Also, something unexpected might come up near the cut-off date, so you should allow some contingency time.

7.1 Answering iCMA questions

When you do the iCMA questions on a unit, you should have the unit and any notes that you made to hand. You will need a pen or pencil, paper, and your calculator. You will also need to go to the M140 website to access the iCMAs.

Make sure that you read each question of an iCMA carefully, so that you understand what is required before you start to work out your answer. You do not have to complete all the questions in an iCMA in one session; you can answer a few questions at a time, in any order, and save your answers. You can also change your answers in later sessions if you wish, before submitting the iCMA. Once you have completed the questions in an iCMA, it is a good idea to read through the questions again, to check that you are happy with your answers and that you have answered as many questions as you can. **Do not submit your iCMA until you are sure you have completed your work on it.** Once you have submitted your iCMA, you will not be able to retrieve it.

In the next activity, you are asked to try the practice quiz for this unit. The quiz is similar in style to the iCMA and the aim of the activity is to familiarise you with the process of answering iCMA questions, before attempting the first iCMA.

Activity 21 *Doing the practice quiz for Unit 1*

There are several versions of the practice quiz: the numbers in each question vary, but the questions are similar. When you start the practice quiz, you get a set of questions chosen at random.

Now go to the M140 website and access the practice quiz for Unit 1. Work through the questions and see how you get on. Unlike an iCMA, you can have as many attempts as you want with the practice quiz. So, if you get the wrong answer first time, you can always have another go – preferably after you've worked out what you did wrong! Return to this unit when you are done.

How did you get on? If you found the quiz difficult, then you may need to revise some topics in the unit, or contact your tutor for help. If you are happy with what you did, you can now start the first iCMA.

Activity 22   *The first iCMA*

Go to the M140 website and find the first iCMA. The first iCMA covers material from Units 1, 2 and 3, so **do not attempt the questions for Units 2 and 3 now**. Your answers are saved automatically when you complete a question, and you can log off and return to the iCMA as you wish. You can change your earlier answers up until the point you submit your iCMA.

You must submit your iCMA before the cut-off date or it will not count, but you can only submit the iCMA once. Hence you should only submit your iCMA once you have finished as much as you can, or if the cut-off date is upon you.

Follow the instructions given on the M140 website and try some of the iCMA questions relating to Unit 1. Complete as many of the questions for Unit 1 as you can. Return to this unit when you are done.

7.2   Answering TMA questions

TMAs are longer pieces of work than iCMAs. Unlike iCMAs, they enable your tutor to assess how you present and explain your statistical ideas, as well as the accuracy of your calculations. There are a few important points to remember when answering a TMA question, illustrated in the following examples and activities.

Example 19 shows why it is important that you show your workings, unless you are specifically asked not to. Good communication is an essential skill and you may lose marks if you do not show your workings.

Example 19   *Showing your workings*

Consider the following extract from a TMA question.

> The following table gives the lengths in centimetres (from tip of bill to tip of tail) for adult British birds of 30 different species.
>
> | 9 | 9 | 12 | 12 | 12 | 13 | 14 | 14 | 14 | 15 | 15 | 16 | 16 | 18 | 21 |
> |----|----|----|----|----|----|----|----|----|----|----|----|----|----|----|
> | 23 | 23 | 24 | 25 | 26 | 27 | 32 | 32 | 34 | 41 | 46 | 46 | 47 | 47 | 64 |
>
> (a) Find the median length of these birds.   [2]
>
> (b) Find the range.   [2]

This question is fairly typical: there are some data, then you are asked to do two things with the data (calculate the median and the range). To the right, the numbers in square brackets tell you how many marks are allocated to each question. Generally, the more marks that are allocated, the more substantial your solution should be.

Consider part (a) of the question. The two marks allocated may include one mark for getting the method right, and one mark for doing the calculation correctly. A correct answer to this question might go something like:

'There are 30 data values, so the median is the average of the 15th and 16th largest values. These are 21 and 23. The average of these values is

$$\frac{21 + 23}{2} = 22.$$

Thus, the median is 22.'

This would get full (that is, two) marks: one for explaining the method and one for getting the right answer. Now consider the following answer:

'The median is 22.'

The answer is certainly correct, so the marker would presume that the right method has been used and therefore award the answer the full two marks. Note that if the question had also stated to 'show your workings', such an answer would *not* get full marks.

However, now consider the following answer:

'The median is 23.'

This answer is incorrect, so loses the accuracy mark. Furthermore, no workings have been shown, so it's impossible to tell whether the student has used the correct method and then made some arithmetic error. Thus such an answer would be awarded zero marks.

Finally, suppose that the student had shown their workings, and produced the following answer:

'There are 30 data values, so the median is the average of the 15th and 16th largest values. These are 21 and 25. The average of these values is

$$\frac{21 + 25}{2} = 23.$$

Thus the median is 23.'

The marker would see that the student has used the right method, but got the 16th largest value wrong. Therefore, the marker would award one mark for method and zero for accuracy. So the student would get one mark for this question.

Example 19 illustrates why it's a good idea to show your workings. In more complicated calculations, a small slip might not cost you all the accuracy marks – provided the marker can see where you've got it wrong. A further reason for showing your workings is that your tutor can then comment on where you went wrong, and provide you with useful feedback. This is much less likely to occur if you don't provide your tutor with something to go on.

Also, sometimes you may be given the answer, and asked to show that this is correct. In this case, all the marks are for method and explanation, and no marks are awarded for getting the correct answer, because it's *already* been given to you.

In the next activity, the tables are turned, and you are asked to mark a student's answer.

Activity 23 *In your tutor's seat*

Suppose you are a tutor marking a student's answer to part (b) of the TMA question in Example 19. You are required to award one mark for using the correct method, and one mark for numerical accuracy.

(a) You are told the correct answer is 55. Work this out for yourself.

(b) The student's answer is as follows:

> 'The range is the difference between the largest and the smallest values. These are 9 and 47, so the range is $47 - 9 = 38$.'

Mark the student's answer.

You will sometimes be asked to interpret your results. Typically, only brief answers are required. Occasionally, different interpretations may be possible, or different features may be picked out as noteworthy. The key point here is to support your interpretation with a brief explanation. This is shown in Example 20.

Example 20 *Answering questions on interpretation*

The following is a continuation of the TMA question described in Example 19.

The bird-size data are shown in the following stemplot.

```
0 | 9 9
1 | 2 2 2 3 4 4 4 5 5 6 6 8
2 | 1 3 3 4 5 6 7
3 | 2 2 4
4 | 1 6 6 7 7
5 |
6 | 4
```

$n = 30$ $0 \mid 9$ represents $9\,\text{cm}$

(c) How many modes are there in this batch? Give a reason for your answer.   [2]

(d) Comment briefly on the shape of this batch.   [2]

A suitable answer to part (c) might be as follows:

> 'There is a single mode at level 1. The small peak at level 4 is probably not significant. Thus, the batch is unimodal.'

This should get full marks, since the interpretation (the batch is unimodal) is supported by a reasonable argument (the peak at level 4 is insignificant).

However, this *is* a matter of judgement. So here is another possible solution:

'There are two modes, at levels 1 and 4. While the peak at level 4 is much smaller than the one at level 1, it may nevertheless be significant. Thus, this batch is bimodal.'

This should also get full marks, because, again, the interpretation (the batch is bimodal) is supported by a reasonable argument (the peak at level 4 might be smaller than that at level 1, but it may still be significant). Statistics is like that: sometimes it can involve judgements that are subjective to some degree. However, the key thing is to support those judgements in such a way that the reader can assess their validity.

Note that you should write your answers out in full sentences, as shown in this example.

Part (d) is an open-ended invitation to comment, which should be kept brief. (It's only worth two marks.) An appropriate answer would be:

'The batch appears to be right-skew, since the higher values are more spread out than the lower values.'

This would get you both marks: one mark for correctly describing it as right-skew and one mark for saying why.

One thing to remember is that 'briefly' really does mean briefly!

Examples 19 and 20 are the subject of Screencast 6 for Unit 1 (see the M140 website).

Here is a final activity on these same data, to give you a bit more practice at answering open-ended questions.

Activity 24   *An open-ended question*

The stemplot in Example 20 can be improved by stretching it, so that each level is split into two.

(a) Construct this stretched stemplot.

(b) Comment briefly on two key aspects of the stretched stemplot that you obtained in part (a).

A further important point in answering TMA questions is to write your answers out as full sentences, even when they include numerical or mathematical expressions. This is important for communicating your answers clearly. It is also a good idea to place each new step within a mathematical calculation on a new line.

One practical reason for communicating clearly is that, otherwise, your tutor might not be able to understand your reasoning, and thus you might lose marks that are awarded for using the correct method.

This advice is also important when reporting on analyses done using Minitab. It is not enough to enclose the Minitab output without further comment, and if you do you may lose marks.

A key step in the modelling diagram, introduced in Subsection 2.1, is to interpret the results of your analyses, and this involves conveying them in properly constructed sentences, not just a computer listing.

4. Interpret

Example 21 *A TMA question with Minitab*

The following is an example of a TMA question that requires the use of Minitab.

(a) Enter the following data into a Minitab spreadsheet. [1]

x	y
81	19
152	33
146	28
86	25
33	14
91	23
123	27
59	17
121	24

Use Minitab to produce a scatterplot of y against x. Include a copy of the scatterplot in the TMA answers that you send to your tutor. [2]

(b) Comment on the relationship between x and y. [2]

Part (a) requires you to use Minitab, and the evidence for what you have done will come from the scatterplot that you send to your tutor. You must make it clear which question the Minitab output relates to. (Do not send more output than is needed to answer the question.) Hence, a satisfactory answer to part (a) would be as follows.

'Scatterplot for part (a):

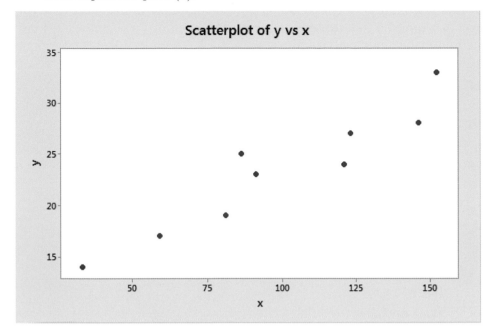

It is a scatterplot of y against x.'

Sending your tutor this scatterplot demonstrates that you know the method for entering data, which would gain one mark, and that you know the method for producing a scatterplot, which gains a second mark. The third mark would require the data to be accurate and the scatterplot to be drawn correctly (y against x and not x against y) with appropriate labels.

A reasonable answer for part (b) might say something like:

'A straight-line graph would be a good way of representing the relationship between y and x as the points lie roughly in a straight line.'

Note that your answer to (b) should be a complete sentence or complete sentences.

When you are working through the units and on your TMA, you are encouraged to seek clarification and help from your tutor or the module forums if you feel you need it. Also, you are encouraged to discuss your work on the module with other students, and to work together in groups if you find this helpful. However, your assignment answers should be your own work, and reflect your own thinking when you do them, even if that thinking has been informed by interactions with others. Your tutor will then be able to assess your progress and provide assistance tailored to your own personal needs if required. What you should not do, if you choose to work with others, is to submit 'group answers'. In addition, you should completely avoid copying answers, unacknowledged, from another source. **This would constitute plagiarism, which is treated severely at the Open University.**

Finally, remember that your tutor is there to offer guidance and support. For this reason, it is worth including partial solutions to questions that you haven't completed, and to send in your TMA even if it's incomplete. This could gain you some marks and some feedback, whereas if you send nothing in, you will receive neither of these.

The following box highlights some of the key points about doing TMAs.

Points to remember when answering TMA questions

- Show your workings – good communication is an important skill.
- Write your answers in full sentences.
- Place each new step in a calculation on a new line.
- Don't just paste computer output – make sure you interpret the output.
- When you interpret results, make sure you support your interpretation.
- Keep your answers brief.
- Your answers should be your own work, and reflect your own thinking.
- TMAs provide an opportunity for you to get marks and feedback, so it's worth sending in incomplete answers.

Summary

In this unit you have been introduced to the components of M140, and to some general ideas about statistical modelling. These are summarised in the modelling diagram, which involves four key steps: posing the question, collecting data, analysing the data, and interpreting the results. You have been reminded of these steps throughout the unit.

You have learned about the need to clean data before analysis, how to round data to specified numbers of decimal places and significant figures, and how to avoid spurious accuracy and rounding errors in calculations. Stemplots were introduced as an effective yet simple way of representing numerical data.

You learned how to construct stretched stemplots, how to recognise and present outliers, and also how to interpret the shape of a batch in terms of modes, symmetry and skewness. The median and range were described, and their resistance to outliers was discussed.

You learned how to use the statistical package Minitab, and how to do calculations on data and obtain stemplots with it. Finally, you worked through a practice quiz in preparation for doing the iCMA on the unit, and learned some key points about completing TMAs.

Learning outcomes

After working through this unit, you should be able to:

- follow the steps of a statistical investigation as set out in the modelling diagram
- recognise that data always need to be carefully inspected, and cleaned if necessary, before further analysis
- round numbers to a given accuracy
- round the final result of a calculation to avoid spurious accuracy
- draw a stemplot of a batch of data
- draw a stemplot in which outliers are listed separately
- draw a stretched stemplot, if appropriate
- use the stemplot of a batch of data to detect peaks (modes)
- use the stemplot of a batch of data to decide whether it is symmetric, left-skew or right-skew
- calculate the median of a batch of data using the stemplot
- find the upper and lower extremes of a batch
- calculate the range of a batch
- interpret the median as a summary measure of the location of a batch
- interpret the range as a summary measure of the spread of a batch
- use your computer to obtain, paste and print material from Minitab windows
- use Minitab to do numerical calculations on data
- use Minitab to obtain and customise stemplots.

Solutions to activities

Solution to Activity 1

No. There are many other possibilities. The next house could be in a different road and so have a completely different number. It may have just a name and no number. The next site could be empty, or perhaps the number 13 was deemed to be unlucky and so was skipped, so that the next house is number 15. Or it could be numbered 11A.

Solution to Activity 2

(a) The curve seems to become less steep as time goes on.

(b) One reason for this is that it is getting harder and harder to find new species of large marine animals. Of course, another reason could be that people are spending less time looking for them – although that seems unlikely. In fact, you'd expect that our ability to discover new species has improved over time.

(c) It seems likely that in the future the curve will become flat. You would expect this to happen once all species have been discovered, and the curve should then remain flat.

Solution to Activity 3

(a) The curve represents the predicted number of large marine species, and so the value 222.94 represents the predicted maximum number of such species. This number really ought to be a whole number, so we 'round it' to the nearest whole number. Thus, the predicted number of large marine species is 223.

(b) In 1996, based on this model, six large marine species were still to be discovered.

(c) These predictions are based on a particular model. Change the model, and the predictions may well change – either up or down. So, for example, if the curve is flattened a little towards the top, then the maximum value would reduce, whereas if the curve were a little steeper, the maximum number would increase.

Solution to Activity 4

Using the relationship between the three quantities, the expenditure for row 4 is
$$\frac{45.13 \times 115.9}{100} = 52.305\,67.$$
So the answer is £52.305 67.

Solution to Activity 5

(a) Rounding to the nearest million means rounding at the position indicated by the vertical bar:

$$6\,985\,|\,119\,415,$$

and the digit to the right of the rounding position is 1. Hence we round down to $6\,985\,000\,000$.

(b) This corresponds to rounding *up* to the nearest ten million.

Solution to Activity 6

(a) The rest of the data in the 'Expenditure' column in Table 2 are given to two decimal places, so we must round the calculated values to two decimal places as well. The rounded value in pounds is 52.31.

(b) The equation in Activity 4 can be rewritten as

$$\text{Petrol price (pence per litre)} = \frac{\text{Expenditure (£)} \times 100}{\text{Petrol used (litres)}}.$$

Substituting the values from row 28 of Table 2, using a calculator we obtain the value of the petrol price to be

$$\frac{54.06 \times 100}{40.37} = 133.911\,3203.$$

The other entries in the table are reported to one decimal place, hence the value should be rounded to one decimal place also. Thus the rounded petrol price in pence per litre is 133.9.

(c) The equation in Activity 4 can also be rewritten as

$$\text{Petrol used (litres)} = \frac{\text{Expenditure (£)} \times 100}{\text{Petrol price (pence per litre)}}.$$

Substituting the values from row 23 gives, on a calculator,

$$\frac{47.70 \times 100}{129.9} = 36.720\,554\,27.$$

Amounts of petrol are given to two decimal places in the table, so two decimal places should be kept, giving the rounded answer in litres as 36.72. The calculation for row 32 gives

$$\frac{57.43 \times 100}{132.9} = 43.212\,942\,06,$$

so the rounded value in litres is 43.21 to two decimal places.

Solution to Activity 7

Multiplying the two numbers, and then rounding to a whole number, gives

$$19.4 \times 23.4 = 453.96 \simeq 454.$$

Rounding first (to 19 and 23) and then multiplying gives

$$19 \times 23 = 437.$$

There is a difference of 17 between these two results. This is a big difference and so this degree of rounding error is unacceptable. The correct result is 453.96, which rounded to a whole number gives 454.

Solution to Activity 8

The mileage was 112 350 on 18.01.10 and 112 616 on 18.02.10, so the distance travelled between these dates was $112\,616 - 112\,350 = 266$ miles.

Solution to Activity 9

(a) 2460 (rounded to the nearest ten) has three significant figures: 2, 4 and 6.

(b) 0.003 610 rounded to six decimal places has four significant figures: 3, 6, 1 and 0.

(c) If the number has been rounded to the nearest ten, then there are two significant figures: 9 and 1. If it has been rounded to the nearest whole number (for example, from 909.8), then there are three: 9, 1 and 0.

(d) To keep three significant figures we round at the positions indicated by the vertical bars:

$$208|.3 \quad \text{and} \quad 0.0983|765.$$

Therefore, the rounded numbers are 208 and 0.0984.

Solution to Activity 10

From Table 2 the mileage value on 18.02.10 was 112 616 and on 04.03.10 it was 112 954. The number of miles travelled between these dates is therefore $112\,954 - 112\,616 = 338$.

The amount of petrol bought on 04.03.10 was 43.49 litres. From the calculator, the quantity of petrol in gallons bought on that date is therefore $43.49/4.546\,09 = 9.566\,462\,609$.

This figure is also the volume of petrol used between the two dates (since the tank was filled up at each petrol stop). The petrol consumption in miles per gallon is therefore:

$$338/9.566\,462\,609 = 35.331\,764\,08,$$

on a calculator. The numbers involved in the calculation, 338, 43.49 and 4.546 09, have three, four and six significant figures respectively, and can all reasonably be considered as having been rounded. Hence we must round our result so that it has three significant figures, so the correctly rounded petrol consumption is 35.3 miles per gallon.

Solution to Activity 11

(a) The stemplot has 17 levels, numbered 26 to 42.

(b) This means that the batch had no values between 27.0 and 27.9, or between 41.0 and 41.9.

(c) Seven levels have a single leaf: levels 30, 31, 33, 34, 37, 40 and 42.

(d) The value 35.3 occurred twice in the batch: the leaf '3' occurs twice at level 35.

Solution to Activity 12

(a) There are no count values below 16 and no count values above 71. Levels 1 to 7 inclusive will therefore suffice. (Level 0 would be needed for counts less than 10, while levels 8 and above would be needed for counts of 80 and more.)

(b) The following figure is the stemplot that results when you proceed from left to right on row 1 of the data, putting the leaves on the stemplot as you go, and then doing the same thing for row 2. (No need to add the key at the bottom for now.)

```
1 | 6 9
2 | 1 4 1 0 1 9 4 2
3 | 9 4 4 7 7
4 | 7 9 6 1 7
5 | 4
6 | 5 7
7 | 1
```

Unordered stemplot for moth-count data

(c) Ordering the leaves on each level, so that they are in increasing numerical order as you move away from the stem, gives the following stemplot.

```
1 | 6 9
2 | 0 1 1 1 2 4 4 9
3 | 4 4 7 7 9
4 | 1 6 7 7 9
5 | 4
6 | 5 7
7 | 1
```

Ordered stemplot for moth-count data

(d) There are 24 data values, so the batch size is $n = 24$. The key is: $1 \mid 6$ represents a count of 16. So the following line should be added to the stemplot:

$n = 24$ $1 \mid 6$ represents a count of 16.

Solution to Activity 13

From the stemplot, you can see that there is a clear tendency for the data values to cluster around level 2, which corresponds to counts in the twenties, with fewer values at higher and lower levels.

The moth counts tail off more gradually towards the higher values, and drop more suddenly towards the lower values.

Solution to Activity 14

From the ordered stemplot the batch size is 24. As this is an even number we must find the middle *two* values, which are the 12th and 13th values. The 12th value, counting from the lowest value, is 34 and the 13th value is 37. So the median value is $(34 + 37)/2 = 35.5$. We must round this to the same level of accuracy as the data values, so the median value is 36.

Solution to Activity 15

(a) Since the levels are 2 to 9, and one leaf digit is retained, we drop the last two digits of each number (without rounding). The data used to construct the stemplot are in the table below. The corresponding stemplot follows after. The outliers are marked *LO* and are 21, corresponding to £2100, and 36, corresponding to £3600.

21	36	55	56	60	65	66	66	69	70
78	83	83	84	87	88	91	96	99	99

```
LO   21 36
  5 | 5 6
  6 | 0 5 6 6 9
  7 | 0 8
  8 | 3 3 4 7 8
  9 | 1 6 9 9
```

$$n = 20 \quad 5 \mid 5 \text{ represents } £5500$$

Stemplot of median salaries for lowest-paid occupations, with low outliers

(b) The batch size is 20, so the median is the average of the 10th and 11th largest values. These are £7000 and £7800, so the average is £7400. (Based on the original data values, the median is £7450.)

(c) If the two lowest groups saw their median salaries rise by £1000, this would not affect the ordering. Therefore, the 10th and 11th values would not be affected and hence the median would stay the same.

Solution to Activity 16

For this batch, $E_U = 114\,000$ and $E_L = 44\,000$ (from the stemplot in Figure 19). Therefore,

$$E_U - E_L = 114\,000 - 44\,000 = 70\,000.$$

So the range is £70 000.

Solution to Activity 17

(a) Dropping the final digit gives the following data. There are two
outliers, 64 and 69. Listing these separately, the stemplot has
levels 1–4, as shown below.

17	18	19	20	22	22	23	23	23
23	25	26	26	27	27	29	30	30
31	32	34	35	40	42	64	69	

```
         1 | 7 8 9
         2 | 0 2 2 3 3 3 3 5 6 6 7 7 9
         3 | 0 0 1 2 4 5
         4 | 0 2
        HI | 64 69
```

$n = 26$ $1 \mid 7$ represents £170

Stemplot of television prices

(b) Splitting each level into two parts gives the following stretched
stemplot.

```
         1 | 7 8 9
         2 | 0 2 2 3 3 3
         2 | 5 6 6 7 7 9
         3 | 0 0 1 2 4
         3 | 5
         4 | 0 2
        HI   64 69
```

$n = 26$ $1 \mid 7$ represents £170

Stretched stemplot of television prices

(c) Splitting each level into five parts gives the following stretched stemplot.

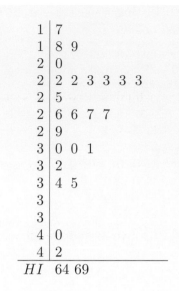

```
            1 | 7
            1 | 8 9
            2 | 0
            2 | 2 2 3 3 3 3
            2 | 5
            2 | 6 6 7 7
            2 | 9
            3 | 0 0 1
            3 | 2
            3 | 4 5
            3 |
            3 |
            4 | 0
            4 | 2
         ──────────────────
           HI  64 69
```

$n = 26$ $1 \mid 7$ represents £170

Another stretched stemplot of television prices

(d) The stemplot in part (a) is perhaps a little too cramped, and the stemplot in part (c) a little too spread out. The stemplot in part (b) satisfies the 'Goldilocks' principle – that is, it's just right! The prices of these televisions cluster around £200–£300, with a couple of high outliers.

Solution to Activity 18

(a) The required stemplot is shown below.

```
   4 | 3 6
   5 | 6 9
   6 | 0 2 2 3 3 3 4 4 4 5 5 5 6 7 7 8 9 9 9 9
   7 | 1 3
```

$n = 26$ $4 \mid 3$ represents 4.3 metres

Stemplot of long jumps

(b) Splitting each level into two parts yields the following stretched stemplot.

```
4 | 3
4 | 6
5 |
5 | 6 9
6 | 0 2 2 3 3 3 4 4 4
6 | 5 5 5 6 7 7 8 9 9 9 9
7 | 1 3
```

$n = 26$ $4 \mid 3$ represents 4.3 metres

Stretched stemplot of long jumps

(c) Splitting each level into five parts gives the stretched stemplot below.

```
4 | 3
4 |
4 | 6
4 |
5 |
5 |
5 |
5 | 6
5 | 9
6 | 0
6 | 2 2 3 3 3
6 | 4 4 4 5 5 5
6 | 6 7 7
6 | 8 9 9 9 9
7 | 1
7 | 3
```

$n = 26$ $4 \mid 3$ represents 4.3 metres

Another stretched stemplot of long jumps

Then, by listing the two low outliers separately, we end up with the subsequent stemplot.

```
LO   43  46
  5 │ 6
  5 │ 9
  6 │ 0
  6 │ 2  2  3  3  3
  6 │ 4  4  4  5  5  5
  6 │ 6  7  7
  6 │ 8  9  9  9  9
  7 │ 1
  7 │ 3
```

$n = 26$ $5 \mid 6$ represents 5.6 metres

Final stemplot of long jumps

(d) The final stemplot is probably the most useful. The stemplot from part (a) is far too cramped, with a large number of values at level 6. The stemplot from part (b) is much better, but still very crowded at the higher levels. The final stemplot gives much more detail.

Solution to Activity 19

(a) Hardly any areas produced less than 4000 thousand tonnes or more than 10 000 thousand tonnes. Most areas produced between 5000 thousand and 9000 thousand tonnes, and somewhere in this range it's possible that there is a single peak, though it's not very strongly marked. If this is correct, then these data are unimodal. If not, then the answer is 'something else'! There's a suggestion that the data are bimodal, though again the peaks are not clear. The honest answer is that in this case, it's rather hard to tell how many modes there are.

(b) These data have one peak at around 48 seconds and another at around 57 seconds, so they are bimodal.

In fact, these times were for both male and female athletes and you can clearly see the two distributions. When there is more than one mode, it is often the case that there are subgroups within the data that can explain the different peaks.

Solution to Activity 20

(a) In the moth-trap data, the larger values are more spread out than the smaller values, so the batch is right-skew.

(b) In the arithmetic test data, the smaller values are more spread out than the larger values, so the batch is left-skew.

Solution to Activity 23

(a) The range is the difference between the largest and the smallest values. These are 64 and 9, so the range is $64 - 9 = 55$.

(b) The numerical value of the answer is wrong, so the student should lose the accuracy mark. However, the method is correct, and the student has just got the wrong 'largest' value. So this answer should be awarded one mark out of the two available.

Solution to Activity 24

(a) The stretched stemplot is as follows.

```
0 | 9 9
1 | 2 2 2 3 4 4 4
1 | 5 5 6 6 8
2 | 1 3 3 4
2 | 5 6 7
3 | 2 2 4
3 |
4 | 1
4 | 6 6 7 7
5 |
5 |
6 | 4
```

$n = 30$ $0 \mid 9$ represents 9 cm

(b) An appropriate answer would be:

'The stemplot is bimodal, with a peak at level 1 and a smaller peak at level 4. The distribution is not symmetric, but it appears to be right-skew, since the higher values are more spread out than the lower values.'

Note that stretching out the stemplot makes it clearer that there may indeed be a second mode – the presence of a second mode is much less apparent in the unstretched stemplot. In an open-ended question like this, there is some scope for what points to focus on. For example, you might choose to mention the possible presence of a high outlier at 64. This would count as another valid 'key aspect'.

Solutions to exercises

Solution to Exercise 1

Your answers may look something like this:

- Collect data: go through past bank statements and extract all items of household expenditure over the past few months, indicating the date, the item, and the amount.
- Analyse data: arrange expenditure items under convenient headings (bills, food, travel, entertainment, etc.), sum them up and then obtain monthly average expenditure totals under each heading.
- Interpret results: critically examine your past expenditure under each heading, and decide upon a strategy to make savings in the future.

Solution to Exercise 2

(a) The discovery curve becoming gradually less steep reflects the fact that times between successive discoveries is increasing as the numbers of species remaining to be discovered decreases.

(b) This could perhaps be used to predict how long it might be expected to take before the next species is discovered. The accuracy of such a prediction might not be very good as improvements in detection techniques might reduce the time until the next discovery. Or, these last few species might be hiding away! And of course, if the last large marine species discovered is in fact the last existing one, the time until the discovery of the next will be infinite.

Solution to Exercise 3

(a) 502.562

(b) 502.561 53

(c) 503

(d) 500.

Solution to Exercise 4

(a) 6 985 120 000, which has six significant figures

(b) 6 985 100 000, which has five significant figures.

Solution to Exercise 5

The petrol used between those two dates is 44.98 litres. The distance travelled is $112\,616 - 112\,350 = 266$ miles. Thus the consumption in litres per 100 kilometres is

$$\frac{100 \times 44.98}{266 \times 1.609\,344} = 10.507\,246\,70.$$

Now 44.98 has four significant figures, 266 has three and the conversion factor has seven. All have been rounded to some extent. The multiplier 100 (which has just one significant figure), on the other hand, has not been rounded, so does not count. So three significant figures should be kept in the final result, which is therefore 10.5 litres per hundred kilometres.

Solution to Exercise 6

(a) Dropping the last digit of each value (without rounding), we obtain the following stemplot.

```
11 | 9
12 | 3  5  7
13 | 8  9
14 | 3
15 | 1  2  4
16 | 2  4  4  7
17 |
18 | 0
```

$$n = 15 \quad 11 \mid 9 \text{ represents } 11.9 \text{ metres}$$

Stemplot for the shot-put data

(b) There are 15 data points, so the median is the 8th largest value. This is 15.1 metres.

(c) The extreme values are $E_L = 11.9$ and $E_U = 18.0$. Therefore, the range is $18.0 - 11.9 = 6.1$ metres.

(d) The distribution clusters around two sets of levels: levels 12–13, and levels 15–16. The maximum value is separated from the rest by a level with no leaves, so could perhaps qualify as an outlier.

Solution to Exercise 7

(a) The following is the first stemplot. There are three outliers: two low outliers at level 1, both corresponding to £1.20, and one high outlier at level 17 corresponding to £17.20.

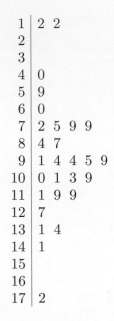

1	2 2
2	
3	
4	0
5	9
6	0
7	2 5 9 9
8	4 7
9	1 4 4 5 9
10	0 1 3 9
11	1 9 9
12	7
13	1 4
14	1
15	
16	
17	2

$n = 28$ 1 │ 2 represents £1.20

Stemplot of wooden toy prices

(b) The following is the stemplot with the outliers listed separately.

LO	12 12
4	0
5	9
6	0
7	2 5 9 9
8	4 7
9	1 4 4 5 9
10	0 1 3 9
11	1 9 9
12	7
13	1 4
14	1
HI	172

$n = 28$ 1 │ 2 represents £1.20

Stemplot of wooden toy prices, with outliers listed separately

(c) There are 28 data values, so the median is the average of the 14th value, 9.4, and the 15th value, 9.5. The average of these two values is 9.45. Rounding to the same accuracy as the other values on the stemplot gives the median to be 9.5.

(d) The lower extreme is 1.2, and the upper extreme is 17.2, so the range is 16.0.

(e) While prices of toys under £20 vary widely, most cluster in the region £7–£11.

Solution to Exercise 8

(a) We drop the last digit (without rounding) and obtain the following stemplot.

```
 8 | 1 2
 9 | 8 9
10 | 0 2 8
11 | 3 3 5
12 | 2 2 3 3
13 | 1 4
```

$n = 16$ 8 | 1 represents 8.1 metres

Stemplot of triple-jump results

(b) Splitting each level into two parts gives the following stretched stemplot.

```
 8 | 1 2
 8 |
 9 |
 9 | 8 9
10 | 0 2
10 | 8
11 | 3 3
11 | 5
12 | 2 2 3 3
12 |
13 | 1 4
```

$n = 16$ 8 | 1 represents 8.1 metres

Stretched stemplot of triple-jump results

(c) The stretched stemplot in part (b), unsurprisingly, is more spread out. It reveals a clustering of values between 9.5 and 12.4 metres which is not immediately apparent in the standard stemplot from part (a). Also, the stretched stemplot reveals some potential low and high outliers, which were not apparent on the standard stemplot.

Solution to Exercise 9

(a) There appear to be two modes, one at level 6 and one at level 8. Thus, these data are bimodal. The data are not symmetric, since the lower values are more spread out than the higher values. The data are left-skew.

(b) There are two modes, one at level 12 and one at level 16. Thus these data are bimodal. If we ignore the high outlier at level 18, the data appear roughly symmetrical around level 14.

Acknowledgements

Grateful acknowledgement is made to the following sources:

Cover image: Minxlj/www.flickr.com/photos/minxlj/422472167/. This file is licensed under the Creative Commons Attribution-Non commercial-No Derivatives Licence http://creativecommons.org/licenses/by-nc-nd/3.0/

Figure 1 Taken from: http://en.wikipedia.org/wiki/File:Mort.svg. This file is licensed under the Creative Commons Attribution-Share Alike Licence http://creativecommons.org/licenses/by-sa/3.0/.

Figure 2 Royal Statistical Society

Figure 6 Richard Ling. http://en.wikipedia.org/wiki/File:Blue_Linckia_Starfish.JPG. This file is licensed under the Creative Commons Attribution-Share Alike Licence http://creativecommons.org/licenses/by-sa/3.0/.

Figure 10 Ilfremer / A.Fifis

Figure 12 With permission from: www.rac.co.uk

Figure 15 Shogo Kato

Figure 17 Trevor & Dilys Pendleton. www.eakringbirds.com

Figure 18 Mike Kemp/In Pictures/Corbis

Figure 25 Taken from: http://en.wikipedia.org/wiki/File:Jessica_Ennis_-_long_jump_-_3.jpg. This file is licensed under the Creative Commons Attribution-Noncommercial-ShareAlike Licence http://creativecommons.org/licenses/by-nc-sa/3.0/.

Figure 29 Taken from: http://thefutureofthings.com/upload/items_icons/Repower-5M-wind-turbine_large.jpg

Subsection 3.2 figure, 'Rounding up', Christopher Furlong / Getty Images

Subsection 5.2 figure, 'Leaning Tower of Pisa' © Jean-Yves Benedeyt.

Every effort has been made to contact copyright holders. If any have been inadvertently overlooked the publishers will be pleased to make the necessary arrangements at the first opportunity.

Unit 2

Prices

Introduction

This unit and Unit 3 examine, in various ways, the question:

Are people getting better or worse off?

Because this is a statistics module, we shall concentrate on the statistical aspects of the question. This unit focuses on statistics about prices, and Unit 3 moves on to consider statistics about earnings; this enables us to look at the question of whether earnings have been increasing more rapidly than prices.

However, it is not the case that statistics can provide all the answers – or even the best answer – to the question of whether people are getting better or worse off. There are many non-statistical issues which are relevant and it is important to put the statistical approach in its correct perspective. To take just one example: if earnings are rising rapidly but unemployment is also rising, then no statistical analysis based on a comparison of earnings with prices will have any relevance to the circumstances of a person who has become unemployed.

In the question examined in these units, *people* does not refer specifically to *you*, Open University students, but to the whole of society in the UK. That is quite a big batch (more than 62 million in 2010, according to an estimate from the UK's Office for National Statistics), consisting of men, women and children, living alone, in large or small households, or in institutions; some of them working, others unemployed, some retired and others not yet old enough for paid work.

It is not possible, using statistical techniques, to provide a complete answer to this one question covering such a big theme, particularly an answer which is valid for all these people and their varied economic and social circumstances; data and techniques both have to be used with common sense. Instead, the aim of these texts is more modest: to explore small batches of data relevant to the question (and relating to some individuals and groups in society), using basic analytical and graphical techniques.

We start with price data and look at some different ways of measuring the overall *location* of a batch of price figures for a single item. In looking for patterns in data, the initial procedures are to round the figures, if necessary, in an appropriate and convenient way, then to draw a stemplot. The next step is to find a measure representing the location of the batch; this will be a value lying between the lowest and highest values of the batch. You have already met one important location measure: the median. (There will be more about this in what follows.) Another very important measure is the *arithmetic mean*, which is introduced in Subsection 1.3.

See Unit 1 – Subsection 3.2, Section 4 and Section 5.

Section 2 shows how to calculate the *weighted mean*, which is a quantity related to the arithmetic mean. You will also learn about some circumstances where it makes sense to calculate a weighted mean.

Having considered the location of a batch, it is often helpful to examine the spread of values and the shape of the distribution of values between the extremes and around the average. Section 3 shows how to calculate one particular measure of spread for a batch: the *interquartile range*. It also shows some diagrammatic methods for representing the spread and shape of the distribution of values in a batch.

Section 4 introduces the notion of a *price index* for indicating changes in the price of a single item and for two or more different items. Section 5 looks at the UK's Retail Prices Index (RPI) and Consumer Prices Index (CPI), which measure changes in prices over time.

The central question, *Are people getting better or worse off?*, is partly addressed in this unit, which focuses on the 'prices' element. If prices are rising, then, other things being equal, we are worse off. It is left to Unit 3 to examine the other important element, 'earnings'. If our earnings are increasing, then, other things being equal, we are better off. However, other things are usually *not* equal – prices and earnings are generally changing at the same time, and Unit 3 also covers the question of how to deal with both sorts of changes at once.

Note that Section 5 is longer than all the other sections, so you should plan your study time accordingly.

Section 6 directs you to the Computer Book. You are also guided to the Computer Book after completing Section 1 and Subsection 2.1. It is better to do the work at those points in the text, although you can leave it until later if you prefer.

1 Measuring location

Measuring location has two components:

- gathering data about the quantity of interest
- determining a value to represent the location of the data.

The task of gathering appropriate data is somewhat problem-specific – general strategies are available, but exact details usually need to be decided for each problem. To determine the price of an electric kettle, for example, we would have to decide the size and type of kettle we're interested in, where and when its purchased, and so forth. In contrast, choosing a value to summarise the location of a set of data is more straightforward. In this section, we will focus on the two most common measures of location: the median and the mean. The data gathered about the quantity of interest does not affect the way we calculate these location measures.

1.1 Data on prices

In order to measure how prices change, we need data on prices and some way of measuring their overall location. Price data take many forms, some of which you have met in Unit 1.

In examining the overall location, prices of all goods are relevant, but some are more important than others. Ballpoint pens are relatively unimportant in most people's shopping baskets, coffee prices are unimportant for tea drinkers, and chicken prices are of little concern to vegetarians. Our first batch of price data is coffee prices (see Table 1).

'Data, data, data!' he cried impatiently. 'I can't make bricks without clay.' (Sherlock Holmes in *The Adventure of the Copper Beeches* by A.C. Doyle (1892))

Example 1 *Jars of coffee*

Table 1 Prices of a 100 g jar of a well-known brand of instant coffee obtained in 15 different shops in Milton Keynes on the same day in February 2012 (in pence, p)

299	315	268	269	295
295	369	275	268	295
279	268	268	295	305

There are several points to note concerning these prices.

- They relate to a particular brand of coffee. You might expect the price to vary between brands.

- They relate to a standard 100 g jar. You might expect the price per gram of this brand of coffee to vary depending upon the size of the jar – larger jars are often cheaper (per gram).

- They relate to a particular locality. You might expect the price to vary depending upon where you buy the coffee (e.g. central London, a suburb, a provincial town, a country village or a Hebridean island).

- They relate to a particular day. You might expect the price to vary from time to time depending upon changes in the cost of raw coffee beans, costs of production and distribution, and the availability of special offers.

Nevertheless, although we have data for a fixed brand of coffee, size of jar, locality and date of purchase, this batch of prices still varies from the lower extreme of 268p to the upper extreme of 369p. (In symbols: $E_L = 268$ and $E_U = 369$.) One of the most likely reasons for this is that the prices were collected from different kinds of shops (e.g. supermarket, petrol station, ethnic grocery and corner shop).

For all these reasons, it is impossible to state exactly what the price of this brand of instant coffee is. Yet its price is, in its own small way, relevant to the question: *Are people getting better or worse off?* That is, if you drink this particular coffee, then changes in its price in your locality will affect your cost of living. Similarly, your costs and economic well-being will also be affected by what happens to the prices of all the other things you need or like to consume.

On the other hand, someone who never buys instant coffee will be unaffected by any change in its price; they will be much more interested in what happens to the prices of alternative products such as ground coffee, tea, milk or fruit juice. The problem of measuring the effect of price changes on individuals with different consumption patterns will be considered in Section 5.

1.2 The median

Example 2 *Picturing the coffee data*

Despite the variability in the data, Table 1 does provide some idea of the price you would expect to pay for a 100 g jar of that particular instant coffee in the Milton Keynes area on that particular day. The information provided by the batch can be seen more clearly when drawn as a stemplot, and this is shown in Figure 1.

```
26 | 8 8 8 8 9
27 | 5 9
28 |
29 | 5 5 5 5 9
30 | 5
31 | 5
32 |
33 |
34 |
35 |
36 | 9
```

$n = 15$ 26 | 8 represents 268 pence

Figure 1 Stemplot of coffee prices from Table 1

This shows at a glance that if you shop around, you might well find this brand of coffee on sale at less than 270p. (Indeed some stores seem to have been 'price matching' at the lowest price of 268p.) On the other hand, if you are not too careful about making price comparisons then you might pay considerably more than 300p (£3). However, you are most likely to find a shop with the coffee priced between about 270p and 300p. Although there is no one price for this coffee, it seems reasonable to say that the overall location of the price is a bit less than 300p.

The **median** of the batch is a useful measure of the overall location of the values in a batch. You met the median in the preceding unit; it was defined as the middle value of a batch of figures when the values are placed in order. Let us revise, and extend slightly, what you learned about the median in Unit 1.

See Subsection 4.2 of Unit 1.

The stemplot in Figure 1 shows the prices arranged in order of size. We can label each of these 15 prices with a symbol indicating where it comes in the ordered batch. A convenient way of showing this is to write each value as the symbol x plus a subscript number in brackets, where the subscript number shows the position of that value within the ordered batch. Figure 2 shows the 15 prices written out in ascending order using this subscript notation.

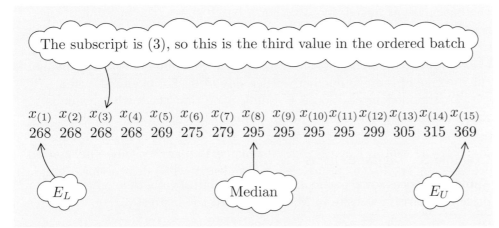

Figure 2 Subscript notation for ordered data

The lower extreme, E_L, is labelled $x_{(1)}$ and the upper extreme, E_U, is labelled $x_{(15)}$. The middle value is the value labelled $x_{(8)}$ since there are as many values, namely 7, above the value of $x_{(8)}$ as there are below it. (This is not *strictly* true here, since the values of $x_{(9)}$, $x_{(10)}$ and $x_{(11)}$ happen also to be actually equal to the median.)

This is illustrated in Figure 3 by a V-shaped formation. The median is the middle value, so it lies at the bottom of the V.

This way of picturing a batch will be developed further in Subsection 3.2.

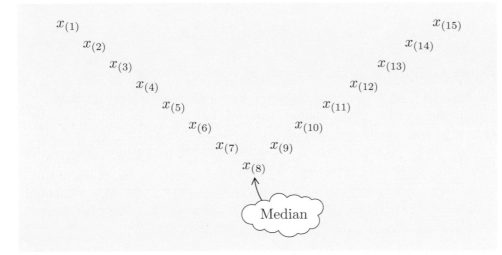

Figure 3 Median of 15 values

An upside down V-shape

If you wanted to make a more explicit statement, then you could write: The median price of this batch of 15 prices is 295p.

If we picture any batch of data as a V-shape like Figure 3, the median of the batch will always lie at the bottom of the V. In the ordered batch, it is more places away from the extremes than any other value.

In general, the median is the value of the middle item when all the items of the batch are arranged in order. For a batch size n, the position of the middle value is $\frac{1}{2}(n+1)$. For example, when $n = 15$, this gives a position of $\frac{1}{2}(15+1) = 8$, indicating that $x_{(8)}$ is the median value. When n is an even number, the middle position is not a whole number and the median is the average of the two numbers either side of it. For example, when $n = 12$, the median position is $6\frac{1}{2}$, indicating that the median value is taken as halfway between $x_{(6)}$ and $x_{(7)}$.

Example 3   *Digital cameras*

Table 2   Prices for a particular model of digital camera as given on a price comparison website in March 2012 (to the nearest £)

60	70	53	81	74
85	90	79	65	70

If we put these prices in order and arrange them in a V-shape, they look like Figure 4.

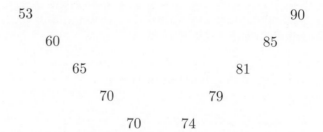

Figure 4   Prices of 10 digital cameras

Because 10 is an even number, there is no single middle value in this batch: the position of the middle item is $\frac{1}{2}(10+1) = 5\frac{1}{2}$. The two values closest to the middle are those shown at the bottom of the V: $x_{(5)} = 70$ and $x_{(6)} = 74$. Their average is 72, so we say that the median price of this batch of camera prices is £72.

Activity 1 *Small flat-screen televisions*

Figure 5 is a stemplot of data on the prices of small flat-screen televisions. (The prices have been rounded to the nearest £10. Originally all but one ended in 9.99, so in this case it makes reasonable sense to ignore the rounding and treat the data as if the prices were exact multiples of £10.) Find the median of these data.

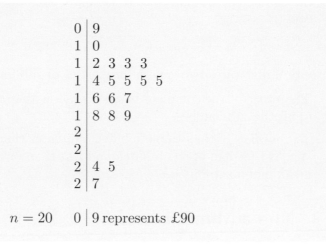

```
0 | 9
1 | 0
1 | 2 3 3 3
1 | 4 5 5 5 5
1 | 6 6 7
1 | 8 8 9
2 |
2 |
2 | 4 5
2 | 7
```

$n = 20$ 0 | 9 represents £90

Not that kind of flat screen

Figure 5 Prices of all flat-screen televisions with a screen size of 24 inches or less on a major UK retailer's website on a day in February 2012

This subsection can now be finished by using some of the methods we have met to examine a batch of data consisting of two parts, or sub-batches.

Activity 2 *The price of gas in UK cities*

Table 3 presents the average price of gas, in pence per kilowatt hour (kWh), in 2010, for typical consumers on credit tariffs in 14 cities in the UK. These cities have been divided into two sub-batches: as seven *northern* cities and seven *southern* cities. (Legally, at the time of writing, Ipswich is a town, not a city, but we shall ignore that distinction here.)

Table 3 Average gas prices in 14 cities

Northern		Southern	
Aberdeen	3.740	Birmingham	3.805
Edinburgh	3.740	Canterbury	3.796
Leeds	3.776	Cardiff	3.743
Liverpool	3.801	Ipswich	3.760
Manchester	3.801	London	3.818
Newcastle-upon-Tyne	3.804	Plymouth	3.784
Nottingham	3.767	Southampton	3.795

(a) Draw a stemplot of all 14 prices shown in the table.

(b) Draw separate stemplots for the seven prices for northern cities and the seven prices for southern cities.

(c) For each of these three batches (northern cities, southern cities and all cities) find the median and the range. Then use these figures to find the general level and the range of gas prices for typical consumers in the country as a whole, and to compare the north and south of the country.

Activity 2 illustrates two general properties of sub-batches:

- The *range* of the complete batch is greater than or equal to the ranges of all the sub-batches.

- The *median* of the complete batch is greater than or equal to the smallest median of a sub-batch and less than or equal to the largest median of a sub-batch.

1.3   The arithmetic mean

Another important measure of location is the arithmetic mean. (Pronounced arith*met*ic.)

> **Arithmetic mean**
>
> The arithmetic mean is the sum of all the values in the batch divided by the size of the batch. More briefly,
>
> $$\text{mean} = \frac{\text{sum}}{\text{size}}.$$

There are other kinds of mean, such as the geometric mean and the harmonic mean, but in this module we shall be using only the arithmetic mean; the word *mean* will therefore normally be used for *arithmetic mean*.

Example 4   *An arithmetic mean*

Suppose we have a batch consisting of five values: 4, 8, 4, 2, 9. In this simple example, the mean is

$$\frac{\text{sum}}{\text{size}} = \frac{4 + 8 + 4 + 2 + 9}{5} = \frac{27}{5} = 5.4.$$

Note that in calculating the mean, the order in which the values are summed is irrelevant.

For a larger batch size, you may find it helpful to set out your calculations systematically in a table. However, in practice the raw data are usually fed directly into a computer or calculator. In general, it is a good idea to check your calculations by reworking them. If possible, use a different method in the reworking; for example, you could sum the numbers in the opposite order.

The formula 'mean = sum/size' can be expressed more concisely as follows. Referring to the values in the batch by x, the 'sum' can be written as $\sum x$. Here $\sum$ is the Greek (capital) letter Sigma, the Greek version of S, and is used in statistics to denote 'the sum of'. Also, the symbol $\overline{x}$ is often used to denote the mean – and as you have already seen in stemplots, n can be used to denote the batch size. (Some calculators use keys marked $\sum x$ and $\overline{x}$ to produce the sum and the mean of a batch directly.)

Using this notation,

$$\text{mean} = \frac{\text{sum}}{\text{size}}$$

can be written as

$$\overline{x} = \frac{\sum x}{n}.$$

In this module we shall normally round the mean to one more figure than the original data.

Activity 3   *Small televisions: the mean*

The prices of 20 small televisions were given in Activity 1 (Subsection 1.2). Find the mean of these prices. Round your answer appropriately (if necessary), given that the original data were rounded to the nearest £10.

1.4 The mean and median compared

Both the mean and median of a batch are useful indicators of the location of the values in the batch. They are, however, calculated in very different ways. To find the median you must first order the batch of data, and if you are not using a computer, you will often do the sorting by means of a stemplot. On the other hand, the major step in finding the mean consists of summing the values in the batch, and for this they do not need to be ordered.

For large batches, at least when you are not using a computer, it is often much quicker to sum the values in the batch than it is to order them. However, for small batches, like some of those you will be analysing in this module without a computer, it can be just as fast to calculate the median as it is to calculate the mean. Moreover, placing the batch values in order is not done solely to help calculate the median – there are many other uses. Drawing a stemplot to order the values also enables us to examine the general shape of the batch, as you saw in Unit 1. In Section 3 you will read about some other uses of the stemplot.

Comparisons based on the method of calculation can be of great practical interest, but the rest of this subsection will consider more fundamental differences between the mean and the median – differences which should influence you when you are deciding which measure to use in summarising the general location of the values in a batch.

Many of the problems with the mean, as well as some advantages, lie in the fact that the precise value of *every* item in the batch enters into its calculation. In calculating the median, most of the data values come into the calculation only in terms of whether they are in the 50% above the median value or the 50% below it. If one of them changes slightly, but without moving into the other half of the batch, the median will not change. In particular, if the extreme values in the batch are made smaller or larger, this will have no effect on the value of the median – the median is resistant to outliers, as noted in Unit 1. In contrast, changes to the extremes could have an appreciable effect on the value of the mean, as the following examples show.

Example 5 *Changing the extreme coffee prices*

For the batch of coffee prices in Figure 1 (Subsection 1.2), the sum of the values is 4363p, so the mean is

$$\frac{4363\text{p}}{15} \simeq 290.9\text{p}.$$

Suppose the highest and lowest coffee prices are reduced so that

$$x_{(1)} = 240 \quad \text{and} \quad x_{(15)} = 340.$$

The median of this altered batch is the same as before, 295p. However, the sum of the values is now 4306p and so the mean is

$$\frac{4306\text{p}}{15} \simeq 287.1\text{p}.$$

Example 6 *Changing the small television prices*

Suppose the highest two television prices in Activity 1 (Subsection 1.2) are altered to £350 and £400. The median, at £150, remains the same as that of the original batch, whereas the new mean is

$$\frac{£3470}{20} = £173.5 \simeq £174$$

compared with the original mean of £162.

Now, even with the very high prices of £350 and £400 for two televisions, the overall location of the main body of the data is still much the same as for the original batch of data. For the original batch the mean, £162, was a reasonably good measure of this. However, for the new batch the mean, £174, is much too high to be a representative measure since, as we can see from the stemplot in Activity 1, most of the values are below £174.

Example 6 is the subject of Screencast 1 for Unit 2 (see the module website).

A measure which is insensitive to changes in the values near the extremes is called a **resistant measure**.

The *median* is a **resistant** measure whereas the *mean* is **sensitive**.

The idea of resistance to outliers was introduced in Subsection 4.2 of Unit 1.

In the following activities, you can investigate some other ways in which the median is *more* resistant than the mean.

Activity 4   *Changing the gas prices*

In Activity 2 (Subsection 1.2) you may have noticed that Cardiff and Ipswich had rather low gas prices compared to the other southern cities. Here you are going to examine the effect of deleting them from the batch of southern cities. Complete the following table and comment on your results.

Batch	Mean	Median
Seven southern cities		
Five southern cities (excluding Cardiff and Ipswich)		

Activity 5   *A misprint in the gas prices*

Suppose the value for London had been misprinted as 8.318 instead of 3.818 (quite an easy mistake to make!). How would this affect your results for the batch of five southern cities (again omitting Cardiff and Ipswich)?

Batch	Mean	Median
Five cities (correct data)		
Five cities (with misprint)		

Suppose you wanted to use these values – the correct ones, of course – to estimate the average price of gas over the whole country. The simple arithmetic mean of the 14 values given in Table 3 would not allow for the fact that much more gas is consumed in London, at a relatively high price, than in other cities. To take account of this you would need to calculate what is known as a *weighted* arithmetic mean. Weighted means are the subject of the next section.

Exercises on Section 1

Exercise 1   *Finding medians*

For each of the following batches of data, find the median of the batch. (We shall also use these batches of data in some of the exercises in Section 3; they come from Figure 37 and Table 11 of Unit 1 (towards the end of Subsections 5.2 and 5.1 respectively).)

(a) Percentage scores in arithmetic:

```
 0 | 7
 1 | 5
 2 |
 3 | 3 5
 4 | 2 2 3
 5 | 5 8
 6 | 4 6 8
 7 | 1 1 6 8 9
 8 | 0 1 1 3 4 5 5 6 9
 9 | 1 1 3 5 9
10 | 0 0
```

$$n = 33 \quad 0 \mid 7 \text{ represents a score of } 7\%$$

(b) Prices of 26 digital televisions (£):

170	180	190	200	220	229	230	230	230
230	250	269	269	270	279	299	300	300
315	320	349	350	400	429	649	699	

Exercise 2   *Finding means*

Calculate the mean for each of the batches in Exercise 1.

Exercise 3   *The effect of removing values on the median and mean*

In the data on prices for small televisions in Activity 1 (Subsection 1.2), the three highest-priced televisions were considerably more expensive than all the others (which all cost under £200). Suppose that in fact these prices had been for a different, larger type of television that should not have been in the batch. (In fact that is not the case – but this is only an exercise!) Leave these three prices out of the batch and calculate the median and the mean of the remaining prices.

How do these values compare with the original median (150) and mean (162)? What does this comparison demonstrate about how resistant the median and mean are?

You have now covered the material needed for Subsection 2.1 of the Computer Book.

2 Weighted means

For goods and services, price changes vary considerably from one to another. Central to the theme question of this unit and the next, *Are people getting better or worse off?*, there is a need to find a fair method of calculating the average price change over a wide range of goods and services. Clearly a 10% rise in the price of bread is of greater significance to most people than a similar rise in the price of clothes pegs, say. What we need to take account of, then, are the relative *weightings* attached to the various price changes under consideration.

2.1 The mean of a combined batch

This first subsection looks at how a mean can be calculated when two unequally weighted batches are combined.

Example 7 *Alan's and Beena's biscuits*

Suppose we are conducting a survey to investigate the general level of prices in some locality. Two colleagues, Alan and Beena, have each visited several shops and collected information on the price of a standard packet of a particular brand of biscuits. They report as follows (Figure 6).

- Alan visited five shops, and calculated that the mean price of the standard packet at these shops was 81.6p.

- Beena visited eight shops, and calculated that the mean price of the standard packet at these shops was 74.0p.

$$\begin{array}{ccc} 74.0 & & 81.6 \\ \vdash & & \vdash \qquad\qquad \longrightarrow \\ & & \text{pence} \end{array}$$

Figure 6 Means of biscuit prices

If we had all the individual prices, five from Alan and eight from Beena, then they could be amalgamated into a single batch of 13 prices, and from this combined batch we could calculate the mean price of the standard packet at all 13 shops. However, our two investigators have unfortunately not written down, nor can they fully remember, the prices from individual shops. Is there anything we can do to calculate the mean of the combined batch?

Fortunately there is, as long as we are interested in arithmetic means. (If they had recorded the medians instead, then there would have been very little we could do.)

The mean of the combined batch of all 13 prices will be calculated as

$$\frac{\text{sum (of the combined batch prices)}}{\text{size (of the combined batch)}}.$$

We already know that the size of the combined batch is the sum of the sizes of the two original batches; that is, $5 + 8 = 13$. The problem here is how to find the sum of the combined batch of Alan's and Beena's prices. The solution is to rearrange the familiar formula

$$\text{mean} = \frac{\text{sum}}{\text{size}}$$

so that it reads

$$\text{sum} = \text{mean} \times \text{size}.$$

This will allow us to find the sums of Alan's five prices and Beena's eight prices separately. Adding the results will produce the sum of the combined batch prices. Finally, dividing by 13 completes the calculation of finding the combined batch mean.

Let us call the sum of Alan's prices 'sum(A)' and the sum of Beena's prices 'sum(B)'.

For Alan: mean = 81.6 and size = 5, so sum(A) = $81.6 \times 5 = 408$.

For Beena: mean = 74.0 and size = 8, so sum(B) = $74.0 \times 8 = 592$.

For the combined batch:

$$\begin{aligned}
\text{mean} &= \frac{\text{combined sum}}{\text{combined size}} \\
&= \frac{408 + 592}{13} \\
&= \frac{1000}{13} \simeq 76.9
\end{aligned}$$

Here, the result has been rounded to give the same number of digits as in the two original means.

The process that we have used above is an important one. It will be used several times in the rest of this unit. The box below summarises the method, using symbols.

> **Mean of a combined batch**
>
> The formula for the **mean $\overline{x}_C$ of a combined batch C** is
> $$\overline{x}_C = \frac{\overline{x}_A n_A + \overline{x}_B n_B}{n_A + n_B},$$
> where batch C consists of batch A combined with batch B, and
> $$\overline{x}_A = \text{mean of batch } A, \quad n_A = \text{size of batch } A,$$
> $$\overline{x}_B = \text{mean of batch } B, \quad n_B = \text{size of batch } B.$$

For our survey in Example 7,

$$\overline{x}_A = 81.6, \quad n_A = 5, \quad \overline{x}_B = 74.0, \quad n_B = 8.$$

The formula summarises the calculations we did as

$$\overline{x}_C = \frac{(81.6 \times 5) + (74.0 \times 8)}{5 + 8}.$$

This expression is an example of a **weighted mean**. The numbers 5 and 8 are the **weights**. We call this expression the weighted mean of 81.6 and 74.0 with weights 5 and 8, respectively.

To see why the term *weighted mean* is used for such an expression, imagine that Figure 7 shows a horizontal bar with two weights, of sizes 5 and 8, hanging on it at the points 81.6 and 74.0, and that you need to find the point at which the bar will balance. This point is at the weighted mean: approximately 76.9.

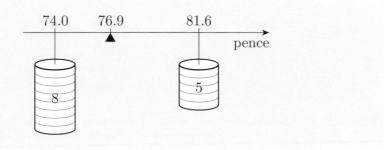

Figure 7   Point of balance at the weighted mean

This physical analogy illustrates several important facts about weighted means.

- It does not matter whether the weights are 5 kg and 8 kg or 5 tonnes and 8 tonnes; the point of balance will be in the same place. It will also remain in the same place if we use weights of 10 kg and 16 kg or 40 kg and 64 kg – it is only the *relative sizes* (i.e. the *ratio*) of the weights that matter.

- The point of balance must be between the points where we hang the weights, and it is nearer to the point with the larger weight.

- If the weights are equal, then the point of balance is halfway between the points.

This gives the following rules.

Rules for weighted means

Rule 1   The weighted mean depends on the relative sizes (i.e. the ratio) of the weights.

Rule 2   The weighted mean of two numbers always lies between the numbers and it is nearer the number that has the larger weight.

Rule 3   If the weights are equal, then the weighted mean of two numbers is the number halfway between them.

Example 8   *Two batches of small televisions*

Suppose that we have two batches of prices (in pounds) for small televisions:

Batch *A* has mean 119 and size 7.

Batch *B* has mean 185 and size 13.

To find the mean of the combined batch we use the formula above, with

$$\overline{x}_A = 119, \quad n_A = 7, \quad \overline{x}_B = 185, \quad n_B = 13.$$

This gives

$$
\begin{aligned}
\overline{x}_C &= \frac{(119 \times 7) + (185 \times 13)}{7 + 13} \\
&= \frac{833 + 2405}{20} \\
&= \frac{3238}{20} \\
&= 161.9 \simeq 162.
\end{aligned}
$$

Note that this is the weighted mean of 119 and 185 with weights 7 and 13 respectively. It lies between 119 and 185 but it is nearer to 185 because this has the greater weight: 13 compared with 7.

Example 8 is the subject of Screencast 2 for Unit 2 (see the module website).

You have also now covered the material needed for Subsection 2.2 of the Computer Book.

2.2   Further uses of weighted means

We shall now look at another similar problem about mean prices – one which is perhaps closer to your everyday experience.

Example 9 *Buying petrol*

Suppose that, in a particular week in 2012, a motorist purchased petrol on two occasions. On the first she went to her usual, relatively low-priced filling station where the price of unleaded petrol was 136.9p per litre and she filled the tank; the quantity she purchased was 41.2 litres. The second occasion saw her obliged to purchase petrol at an expensive service station where the price of unleaded petrol was 148.0p per litre; she therefore purchased only 10 litres. What was the mean price, in pence per litre, of the petrol she purchased during that week?

To calculate this mean price we need to work out the total expenditure on petrol, in pence, and divide it by the total quantity of petrol purchased, in litres.

The total quantity purchased is straightforward as it is just the sum of the two quantities, so $41.2 + 10$.

To find the expenditure on each occasion, we need to apply the formula:

$$\text{cost} = \text{price} \times \text{quantity}.$$

This gives 136.9×41.2 and 148.0×10, respectively.

So the total expenditure, in pence, is $(136.9 \times 41.2) + (148.0 \times 10)$. The mean price, in pence per litre, for which we were asked, is this total expenditure divided by the total number of litres bought:

$$\frac{(136.9 \times 41.2) + (148.0 \times 10)}{41.2 + 10}.$$

We have left the answer in this form, rather than working out the individual products and sums as we went along, to show that it has the same form as the calculation of the combined batch mean. (The answer is 139.07p per litre, rounded from 139.067 97p per litre.)

The phrase 'goods and services' is an awkward way of referring to the things that are relevant to the cost of living; that is, physical things you might buy, such as bread or gas, and services that you might pay someone else to do for you, such as window-cleaning. Economists sometimes use the word *commodity* to cover both goods and services that people pay for, and we shall use that word from time to time in this unit. (Note that there are other, different, technical meanings of commodity that you might meet in different contexts.)

> **The mean price of a quantity bought on two different occasions**
>
> In general, if you purchase q_1 units of some commodity at p_1 pence per unit and q_2 units of the same commodity at p_2 pence per unit, then the mean price of this commodity, $\bar{p}$ pence per unit, can be calculated from the following formula:
>
> $$\bar{p} = \frac{p_1\,q_1 + p_2\,q_2}{q_1 + q_2}.$$

Example 10   *Buying potatoes*

Suppose that, in one month, a family purchased potatoes on two occasions. On one occasion they bought 10 kg at 40p per kg, and on another they bought 6 kg at 45p per kg. We can use this formula to calculate the mean price (in pence per kg) that they paid for potatoes in that month. We have

$$\left. \begin{array}{ll} q_1 = 10 & \text{quantity} \\ p_1 = 40 & \text{price} \end{array} \right\} \text{first occasion}$$

and

$$\left. \begin{array}{ll} q_2 = 6 & \text{quantity} \\ p_2 = 45 & \text{price} \end{array} \right\} \text{second occasion.}$$

This gives

$$\begin{aligned} \bar{p} &= \frac{(40 \times 10) + (45 \times 6)}{10 + 6} \\ &= \frac{400 + 270}{16} \\ &= \frac{670}{16} \\ &= 41.875 \simeq 41.9. \end{aligned}$$

So the mean price for that month is 41.9p per kg.

The two formulas we have been using,

$$\frac{\bar{x}_A n_A + \bar{x}_B n_B}{n_A + n_B} \quad \text{and} \quad \frac{p_1 q_1 + p_2 q_2}{q_1 + q_2},$$

are basically the same; they are both examples of weighted means.

The first formula is the weighted mean of the numbers $\bar{x}_A$ and $\bar{x}_B$, using the batch sizes, n_A and n_B, as weights.

The second formula is the weighted mean of the unit prices p_1 and p_2, using the quantities bought, q_1 and q_2, as weights.

The general form of a weighted mean of two numbers having associated weights is as follows.

> **Weighted mean of two numbers**
>
> The **weighted mean** of the two numbers x_1 and x_2 with corresponding weights w_1 and w_2 is
>
> $$\frac{x_1 w_1 + x_2 w_2}{w_1 + w_2}.$$

Weighted means have many uses, two of which you have already met. The type of weights depends on the particular use. In our uses, the weights were the following.

- The sizes of the batches, when we were calculating the combined batch mean from two batch means.

- The quantities bought, when we were calculating the mean price of a commodity bought on two separate occasions.

Another very important use is in the construction of an index, such as the Retail Prices Index; we shall therefore be making much use of weighted means in the final sections of this unit.

In the next example, we do not have all the information required to calculate the mean, but we can still get a reasonable answer by using weights.

Example 11 *Weighted means of two gas prices*

Let us return to the gas prices in Table 3 (Subsection 1.2). This has information about the price of gas for typical consumers in individual cities, but no national figure. Suppose that you want to combine these figures to get an average figure for the whole country; how could you do it? At the end of Section 1, it was suggested that weighted means could provide a solution. The complete answer to this question, using weighted means, is in Example 13 towards the end of this section. To introduce the method used there, let us now consider a similar, but simpler, question.

Here we use just two cities, London and Edinburgh, where the prices were 3.818p per kWh and 3.740p per kWh respectively. How can we combine these two values into one sensible average figure?

One possibility would be to take the simple mean of the two numbers. This gives

$$\tfrac{1}{2}(3.818 + 3.740) = 3.779.$$

However, this gives both cities *equal* weight. Because London is a lot larger than Edinburgh, we should expect the average to be nearer the London price than the Edinburgh price.

This suggests that we use a *weighted* mean of the form

$$\frac{3.818q_1 + 3.740q_2}{q_1 + q_2},$$

where q_1 and q_2 are suitably chosen weights, with the weight q_1 of the London price larger than the weight q_2 of the Edinburgh price.

The best weights would be the total quantities of gas consumed in 2010 in each city. However, even if this information is not available to us, we can still find a reasonable average figure by using as weights a readily available measure of the sizes of the two cities: their populations.

The populations of the urban areas of these cities are approximately 8 300 000 and 400 000 respectively. So we could put $q_1 = 8\,300\,000$ and $q_2 = 400\,000$.

However, we know that the weighted mean depends only on the ratio of the weights. Therefore, the weights $q_1 = 83$ and $q_2 = 4$ will give the same answer.

These weights give

$$\frac{(3.818 \times 83) + (3.740 \times 4)}{83 + 4}.$$

Activity 6   *Using the rules for weighted means*

Using the rules for weighted means, would you expect the weighted mean price to be nearer the London price or the Edinburgh price? To check, calculate the weighted mean price.

Although we cannot think of the weighted mean price in Activity 6 as a calculation of the total cost divided by the total consumption, the answer *is* an estimate of the average price, in pence per kWh, for typical consumers in the two cities, and it is the best estimate we can calculate with the available information.

Sometimes the weights in a weighted mean do not have any significance in themselves: they are neither quantities, nor sizes, etc., but simply weights. This is illustrated in the following activity.

Activity 7   *Weighted means of Open University marks*

As an Open University student, an example of the use of weighted means with which you are familiar, or will soon become familiar, is the combination of interactive computer-marked assignment (iCMA) and tutor-marked assignment (TMA) scores to provide an overall continuous assessment score (OCAS).

Suppose that you obtain a score of 80 for your iCMAs and a score of 60 for your TMAs. (I am not saying these are typical scores for M140!) Calculate what your overall continuous assessment score will be if the weights for the two components are as follows.

(a) iCMA 50, TMA 50

(b) iCMA 40, TMA 60

(c) iCMA 65, TMA 55

(d) iCMA 25, TMA 75

(e) iCMA 30, TMA 90

We have seen, in Activity 7 and in Example 11, that only the ratio of the weights affects the answer, not the individual weights. So weights are often chosen to add up to a convenient number like 100 or 1000.

> This is Rule 1 for weighted means (see Subsection 2.1).

Activity 7 should also have reminded you of another important property of a weighted mean of two numbers: the weighted mean lies nearer to the number having the larger weight.

> This is part of Rule 2 for weighted means.

2.3 More than two numbers

The idea of a weighted mean can be extended to more than two numbers. To see how the calculation is done in general, remind yourself first how we calculated the weighted mean of two numbers x_1 and x_2 with corresponding weights w_1 and w_2.

1. Multiply each number by its weight to get the products $x_1 w_1$ and $x_2 w_2$.

2. Sum these products to get $x_1 w_1 + x_2 w_2$.

3. Sum the weights to get $w_1 + w_2$.

4. Divide the sum of the products by the sum of the weights.

This leads to the following formula.

> **Weighted mean of two or more numbers**
>
> The weighted mean of two or more numbers is
> $$\frac{\text{sum of \{number} \times \text{weight\}}}{\text{sum of weights}} = \frac{\text{sum of products}}{\text{sum of weights}}.$$

This is the formula which is used to find the weighted mean of any set of numbers, each with a corresponding weight.

Example 12 *A weighted mean of wine prices*

Suppose we have the following three batches of wine prices (in pence per bottle).

Batch 1 with mean 525.5 and batch size 6.

Batch 2 with mean 468.0 and batch size 2.

Batch 3 with mean 504.2 and batch size 12.

We want to calculate the weighted mean of these three batch means using, as corresponding weights, the three batch sizes. Rather than applying the formula directly, the calculations can be set out in columns.

Table 4 Data on wine purchases

Batch	Number (batch mean)	Weight (batch size)	Number × weight (= product)
Batch 1	525.5	6	3 153.0
Batch 2	468.0	2	936.0
Batch 3	504.2	12	6 050.4
Sum		20	10 139.4

The weighted mean is

$$\frac{\text{sum of products}}{\text{sum of weights}} = \frac{10\,139.4}{20} = 506.97.$$

We round this to the same accuracy as the original means, to get a weighted mean of 507.0. (Note that this lies between 468.0 and 525.5. This is a useful check, as a weighted mean always lies within the range of the original means.)

The physical analogy in Example 12 can be extended to any set of numbers and weights. Suppose that you calculate the weighted mean for:

1.3 with weight 2

1.9 with weight 1

1.7 with weight 3.

This is given by

$$\frac{(1.3 \times 2) + (1.9 \times 1) + (1.7 \times 3)}{2 + 1 + 3} = \frac{2.6 + 1.9 + 5.1}{6} = \frac{9.6}{6} = 1.6.$$

This is pictured in Figure 8, with the point of balance for these three weights shown at 1.6.

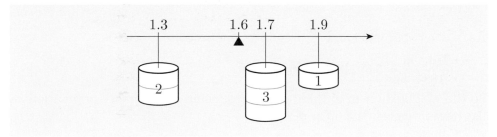

Figure 8 Point of balance for three means

You will meet many examples of weighted means of larger sets of numbers in Subsection 5.2, but we shall end this section with one more example.

Example 13 *Weighted means of many gas prices*

Example 11 showed the calculation of a weighted mean of gas prices using, for simplicity, just the two cities London and Edinburgh. We can extend Example 11 to calculate a weighted mean of all 14 gas prices from Table 3, using as weights the populations of the 14 cities. The calculations are set out in Table 5.

Table 5 Product of gas price and weight by city

	Price (p/kWh) x	Weight w	Price × weight xw
Aberdeen	3.740	19	71.060
Edinburgh	3.740	42	157.080
Leeds	3.776	150	566.400
Liverpool	3.801	82	311.682
Manchester	3.801	224	851.424
Newcastle-upon-Tyne	3.804	88	334.752
Nottingham	3.767	67	252.389
Birmingham	3.805	228	867.540
Canterbury	3.796	5	18.980
Cardiff	3.743	33	123.519
Ipswich	3.760	14	52.640
London	3.818	828	3161.304
Plymouth	3.784	24	90.816
Southampton	3.795	30	113.850
Sum		1834	6973.436

The entries in the weight column, w, are the approximate populations, in 10 000s, of the urban areas that include each city (as measured in the 2001 Census). For each city, we multiply the price, x, by the weight, w, to get the entry in the last column, xw.

The weighted mean of the gas prices using these weights is then

$$\frac{\text{sum of products (price} \times \text{weight)}}{\text{sum of weights}}$$

or, in symbols,

$$\frac{\sum xw}{\sum w}.$$

As $\sum xw = 6973.436$ and $\sum w = 1834$, the weighted mean is

$$\frac{6973.436}{1834} = 3.802\,310 \simeq 3.802.$$

So the weighted mean of these gas prices, using approximate population figures as weights, is 3.802p per kWh.

Note that this weighted mean is larger than all but three of the gas prices for individual cities. That is because the cities with the two highest populations, London and Birmingham, also have the highest gas prices, and the weighted mean gas price is pulled towards these high prices.

Although the details of the calculation above are written out in full in Table 5, in practice, using even a simple calculator, this is not necessary. It is usually possible to keep a running sum of both the weights and the products as the data are being entered. One way of doing this is to accumulate the sum of the weights into the calculator's memory while the sum of the products is cumulated on the display. If you are using a specialist statistics calculator, the task is generally very straightforward. Simply enter each price and its corresponding weight using the method described in your calculator instructions for finding a weighted mean.

Activity 8   *Weighted means on your calculator*

Use your calculator to check that the sum of weights and sum of products of the data in Table 5 are, respectively, 1834 and 6973.436, and that the weighted mean is 3.802. (No solution is given to this activity.)

Activity 9   *Weighted mean electricity price*

Table 6 is similar to Table 5, but this time it presents the average price of *electricity*, in pence per kilowatt hour (kWh). These data are again for the year 2010 for typical consumers on credit tariffs in the same 14 cities we have been considering for gas prices, with the addition of Belfast. Again, the weights are the approximate populations of the relevant urban areas, in 10 000s.

Table 6   Populations and electricity prices in 15 cities

	Price (p/kWh) x	Weight w	Price × weight xw
Aberdeen	13.76	19	
Belfast	15.03	58	
Edinburgh	13.86	42	
Leeds	12.70	150	
Liverpool	13.89	82	
Manchester	12.65	224	
Newcastle-upon-Tyne	12.97	88	
Nottingham	12.64	67	
Birmingham	12.89	228	
Canterbury	12.92	5	
Cardiff	13.83	33	
Ipswich	12.84	14	
London	13.17	828	
Plymouth	13.61	24	
Southampton	13.41	30	
Sum			

Use these data to calculate the weighted mean electricity price. (Your calculator will almost certainly allow you to do this without writing out all the values in the xw column.)

Exercises on Section 2

Exercise 4   *A combined batch of camera prices*

Find the mean price of the batch formed by combining the following two batches, A and B, of camera prices.

Batch A has mean price £80.7 and batch size 10.

Batch B has mean price £78.5 and batch size 17.

Exercise 5 *The mean price of fabric*

Suppose you buy 8.5 metres of fabric in a sale, at £10.95 per metre, to make some bedroom curtains. The following year you decide to make a matching bedspread and so you buy 6 metres of the same material, but the price is now £12.70 per metre. Calculate the mean price of all the material, in £ per metre.

3 Measuring spread

As you have already seen, it is difficult to measure price changes when they so often vary from shop to shop and region to region. Taking some average value, such as the median or the mean, helps to simplify the problem. However, it would be a mistake to ignore the notion of spread, as averages on their own can be misleading.

Information about spread can be very important in statistical analysis, where you are often interested in comparing two or more batches. In this section we shall look first at measures of spread, and then at some methods of summarising the shape of a batch of data.

But how can spread be measured? Just as there are several ways of measuring location (mean, median, etc.), there are also several ways of measuring spread. Here, we shall examine two such measures: the *range* and the *interquartile range*.

In the next unit you will learn about a further measure of spread called the *standard deviation*.

3.1 The range

You have already met the range, which is defined below.

I like to sleep each night with my feet in the oven and my head in the freezer. That way I'm comfortable on average.

See Subsection 4.2 of Unit 1.

> **The range**
>
> The range is the distance between the lower and the upper extremes. It can be calculated from the formula:
>
> $$\text{range} = E_U - E_L,$$
>
> where E_U is the upper extreme and E_L is the lower extreme.

Given an ordered batch of data, for example in a stemplot, the range can easily be calculated. However, the range tells us very little about how the values in the main body of the data are spread. It is also very sensitive to changes in the extreme values, like those considered in Subsection 1.4. It would be better to have a measure of spread that conveys more information about the spread of values in the main body of the data. One such measure is based upon the difference between two particular values in the batch, known as the **quartiles**. As the name suggests, the two quartiles lie one quarter of the way into the batch from either end. The major part of the next subsection describes how to find them.

3.2 Quartiles and the interquartile range

Finding the quartiles of a batch is very similar to finding the median.

In Subsection 1.2, we represented a batch as a V-shaped formation, with the median at the 'hinge' where the two arms of the V meet. The median splits the batch into two equal parts. Similarly, we can put another hinge in each side of the V and get four roughly equal parts, shaped like this: ⋀. For a batch of size 15, it looks like Figure 9.

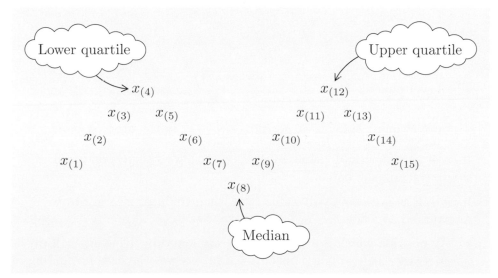

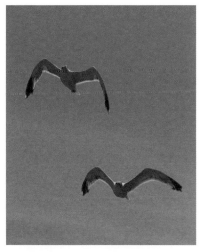

More birds, now showing the shape of the ⋀ diagram

Figure 9   Median and quartiles

The points at the side hinges, in this case $x_{(4)}$ and $x_{(12)}$, are the quartiles. There are two quartiles which, as with the extremes, we call the **lower quartile** and the **upper quartile**. The lower quartile separates off the bottom quarter, or lowest 25%. The upper quartile separates off the top quarter, or highest 25%. They are denoted Q_1 and Q_3 respectively. (Sometimes they are referred to as the *first quartile* and the *third quartile*.)

You might be wondering, if these are Q_1 and Q_3, what happened to Q_2? Well, have a think about that for a moment.

Q_1 separates the bottom quarter of the data (from the top three quarters), and Q_3 separates the bottom three quarters (from the top quarter). So it would make sense to say that Q_2 separates the bottom two quarters (from the top two quarters). But two quarters make a half, so Q_2 would denote the median, and since there is already a separate word for that, it's not usual to call it the second quartile.

Usually we cannot divide the batch exactly into quarters. Indeed, this is illustrated in Figure 9 where the two central parts of the $\wedge\wedge$ are larger than the outer ones. As with calculating the median for an even-sized batch, some rule is needed to tell us how many places we need to count along from the smallest value to find the quartiles. However, there are several alternatives that we could adopt and the particular rule described below is somewhat arbitrary. Different authors and different software may use slightly different rules. The rule adopted here is the one used by Minitab. If your calculator can find quartiles, note that it may use a different rule, and you may also have used different rules in other Open University modules.

As you might have expected, the rule involves dividing $(n + 1)$ by 4, where n is the batch size (as opposed to dividing by 2 to find the median). However, the rule is slightly more complicated for the quartiles and it depends on whether $n + 1$ is exactly divisible by 4.

The quartiles

The lower quartile Q_1 is at position $\dfrac{(n+1)}{4}$ in the ordered batch.

The upper quartile Q_3 is at position $\dfrac{3(n+1)}{4}$ in the ordered batch.

If $(n + 1)$ is exactly divisible by 4, these positions correspond to a single value in the batch.

If $(n + 1)$ is *not* exactly divisible by 4, then the positions are to be interpreted as follows.

- A position which is a whole number followed by $\frac{1}{2}$ means 'halfway between the two positions either side' (as was the case for finding the median).

- A position which is a whole number followed by $\frac{1}{4}$ means 'one quarter of the way from the position below to the position above'. So for instance if a position is $5\frac{1}{4}$, the quartile is the number one quarter of the way from $x_{(5)}$ to $x_{(6)}$.

- A position which is a whole number followed by $\frac{3}{4}$ means 'three quarters of the way from the position below to the position above'. So for instance if a position is $4\frac{3}{4}$, the quartile is the number three quarters of the way from $x_{(4)}$ to $x_{(5)}$.

Before we actually use these rules to find quartiles, let us look at some more examples of $\wedge\wedge$-shaped diagrams for different batch sizes n. The case where $(n + 1)$ is exactly divisible by 4, so that $\frac{1}{4}(n + 1)$ is a whole number, was shown in Figure 9. The following three figures show the three other possible scenarios, where $(n + 1)$ is not exactly divisible by 4.

For $n = 17$, $\frac{1}{4}(n+1) = 4\frac{1}{2}$ and $\frac{3}{4}(n+1) = 13\frac{1}{2}$. So Q_1 is halfway between $x_{(4)}$ and $x_{(5)}$, and Q_3 is halfway between $x_{(13)}$ and $x_{(14)}$.

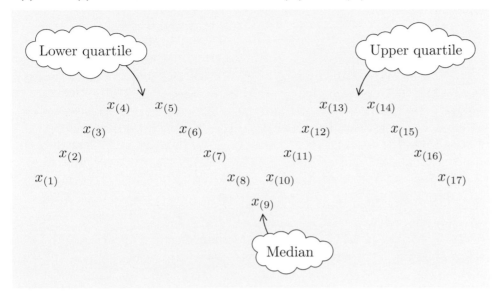

Figure 10   Quartiles for sample size $n = 17$

For $n = 18$, $\frac{1}{4}(n+1) = 4\frac{3}{4}$ and $\frac{3}{4}(n+1) = 14\frac{1}{4}$. So Q_1 is three quarters of the way from $x_{(4)}$ to $x_{(5)}$, and Q_3 is one quarter of the way from $x_{(14)}$ to $x_{(15)}$.

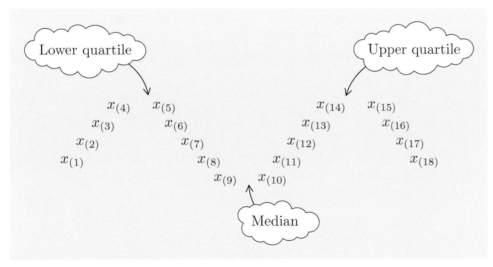

Figure 11   Quartiles for sample size $n = 18$

For $n = 20$, $\frac{1}{4}(n+1) = 5\frac{1}{4}$ and $\frac{3}{4}(n+1) = 15\frac{3}{4}$. So Q_1 is one quarter of the way from $x_{(5)}$ to $x_{(6)}$, and Q_3 is three quarters of the way from $x_{(15)}$ to $x_{(16)}$.

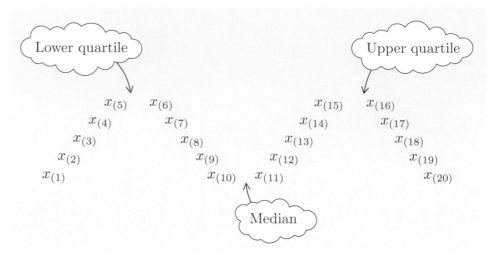

Figure 12   Quartiles for sample size $n = 20$

Example 14   *Quartiles for the prices of small televisions*

Figure 12 showed you where the quartiles are for a batch of size 20. Let us now use the stemplot of the 20 television prices in Figure 13, which you first met in Figure 5 (Subsection 1.2), to find the lower and upper quartiles, Q_1 and Q_3, of this batch.

```
0 | 9
1 | 0
1 | 2 3 3 3
1 | 4 5 5 5 5
1 | 6 6 7
1 | 8 8 9
2 |
2 |
2 | 4 5
2 | 7
```

$$n = 20 \quad 0 \,|\, 9 \text{ represents £90}$$

Figure 13   Prices of flat-screen televisions with a screen size of 24 inches or less

To calculate the lower quartile Q_1 you need to find the number that is one quarter of the way from $x_{(5)}$ to $x_{(6)}$. These values are both 130, so Q_1 is 130. To calculate the upper quartile Q_3 you need to find the number three quarters of the way from $x_{(15)}$ to $x_{(16)}$. These values are both 180, so Q_3 is 180.

That example was easier than it might have been, because for each quartile the two numbers we had to consider turned out to be equal!

Example 15 *Quartiles for the camera prices*

Table 2 (Subsection 1.2) gave ten prices for a particular model of digital camera (in pounds). In order, the prices are as follows.

| 53 | 60 | 65 | 70 | 70 | 74 | 79 | 81 | 85 | 90 |

To find the lower and upper quartiles, Q_1 and Q_3, of this batch, first find $\frac{1}{4}(n+1) = 2\frac{3}{4}$ and $\frac{3}{4}(n+1) = 8\frac{1}{4}$.

The lower quartile Q_1 is the number three quarters of the way from $x_{(2)}$ to $x_{(3)}$. These values are 60 and 65. The difference between them is $65 - 60 = 5$, and three quarters of that difference is $\frac{3}{4} \times 5 = 3.75$. Therefore Q_1 is 3.75 larger than 60, so it is 63.75. As with the median, in this module we will generally round the quartiles to the accuracy of the original data, so in this case we round to the nearest whole number, 64. In symbols, $Q_1 = 60 + \frac{3}{4}(65 - 60) = 63.75 \simeq 64$.

The upper quartile Q_3 is the number one quarter of the way from $x_{(8)}$ to $x_{(9)}$. These values are 81 and 85. The difference between them is $85 - 81 = 4$, and one quarter of that difference is $\frac{1}{4} \times 4 = 1$. Therefore Q_3 is 1 larger than 81, so it is 82. (No rounding necessary this time.) In symbols, $Q_3 = 81 + \frac{1}{4}(85 - 81) = 82$.

Example 15 is the subject of Screencast 3 for Unit 2 (see the module website).

Activity 10   *Finding more quartiles*

(a) Find the lower and upper quartiles of the batch of 15 coffee prices in Figure 14. (This batch of coffee prices was first introduced in Table 1 of Subsection 1.1.)

```
26 | 8 8 8 8 9
27 | 5 9
28 |
29 | 5 5 5 5 9
30 | 5
31 | 5
32 |
33 |
34 |
35 |
36 | 9
```

$n = 15$ $26 \mid 8$ represents 268 pence

Figure 14   Stemplot of 15 coffee prices

(b) Find the lower and upper quartiles of the batch of 14 gas prices in Figure 15. (This batch of gas prices was first introduced in Table 3 of Subsection 1.2.)

```
374 | 0 0 3
375 |
376 | 0 7
377 | 6
378 | 4
379 | 5 6
380 | 1 1 4 5
381 | 8
```

$n = 14$ $374 \mid 0$ represents 3.740p per kWh

Figure 15   Stemplot of 14 gas prices

A measure of spread

Now we can define a new measure of spread based entirely on the lower and upper quartiles.

The interquartile range

The interquartile range (sometimes abbreviated to **IQR**) is the distance between the lower and upper quartiles:

$$IQR = Q_3 - Q_1.$$

Note that this value is independent of the sizes of E_U and E_L.

Example 16   *The prices of small televisions, yet again!*

For the batch of 20 television prices in Example 14,

$$IQR = Q_3 - Q_1$$
$$= 180 - 130$$
$$= 50.$$

So the interquartile range is £50.

Activity 11   *Coffee prices again*

Calculate both the range and the interquartile range of the batch of 15 coffee prices, last seen in Figure 14.

Activity 12   *Interquartile range of gas prices*

In Activity 10(b) you found the quartiles of the 14 gas prices from Activity 2 (Subsection 1.2). Find the interquartile range.

You may be wondering why you are being asked to learn a new measure of spread when you already know the range. As a measure of spread, the range ($E_U - E_L$) is not very satisfactory because it is not resistant to the effects of unrepresentative extreme values. The interquartile range, by contrast, is a highly resistant measure of spread (because it is not sensitive to the effects of values lying outside the middle 50% of the batch) and it is generally the preferred choice.

Resistant measures were explained in Subsection 1.4.

Example 17   *Comparing the resistance of the range and the IQR*

Suppose the price of the most expensive jar of coffee is reduced from 369p to 325p. How does this affect the range and the interquartile range of the batch of coffee prices in Figure 14?

The new range is

$$E_U - E_L = 325p - 268p = 57p,$$

a lot less than the original value of 101p (found in Activity 11). The interquartile range is unchanged.

3.3   The five-figure summary and boxplots

As well as giving us a new measure of spread – the interquartile range – the quartiles are important figures in themselves. Our ∧∧-shaped diagram, Figure 16, gives five important points which help to summarise the shape of a distribution: the **median**, the **two quartiles** and the **two extremes**.

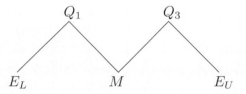

Figure 16   Values in a five-figure summary

These are conveniently displayed in the following form, called the **five-figure summary** of the batch.

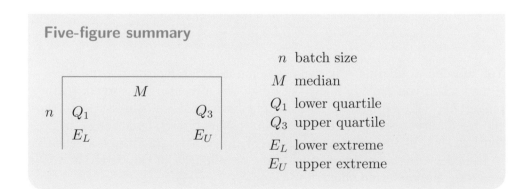

Five-figure summary

n batch size

M median

Q_1 lower quartile

Q_3 upper quartile

E_L lower extreme

E_U upper extreme

Example 18   *Five-figure summary for television price data*

For the television price data, we have $n = 20$, $M = 150$, $Q_1 = 130$, $Q_3 = 180$, $E_L = 90$ and $E_U = 270$.

You last saw these data in Figure 13.

Therefore, the five-figure summary of this batch is

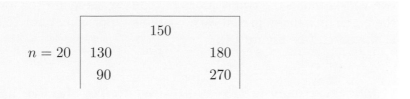

This diagram contains the following information about the batch of prices.

- The general level of prices, as measured by the median, is £150.
- The individual prices vary from £90 to £270.
- About 25% of the prices were less than £130.
- About 25% of the prices were more than £180.
- About 50% of the prices were between £130 and £180.

We hope you agree that the five-figure summary is quite an efficient way of presenting a summary of a batch of data.

The five values in a five-figure summary can be very effectively presented in a special diagram called a **boxplot**. For the 14 gas prices (Figure 15) the diagram looks like Figure 17.

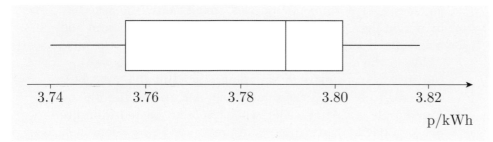

Figure 17   Boxplot of batch of 14 gas prices

The central feature of this diagram is a *box* – hence the name *box*plot. The box extends from the *lower quartile* (at the left-hand edge of the box) to the *upper quartile* (the right-hand edge). This part of the diagram contains 50% of the values in the batch. The length of this box is thus the *interquartile range*.

Outside the box are two *whiskers*. (Boxplots are sometimes called *box-and-whisker diagrams*.) In many cases, such as in Figure 17, the whiskers extend all the way out to the extremes. Each whisker then covers the end 25% of the batch and the distance between the two whisker-ends is then the *range*. (You will see examples later where the whiskers do not go right out to the extremes.)

So far we have dealt with four figures from the five-figure summary: the two quartiles and the two extremes. The remaining figure is perhaps the most important: it is the *median*, whose position is shown by putting a vertical line through the box.

Thus a boxplot shows clearly the division of the data into four parts: the two whiskers and the two sections of the box; these are the four parts of the ∧∧-shaped diagram and each contains (approximately) 25% of values in the batch (see Figure 18).

John Tukey teaching at Princeton University

John W. Tukey (1915–2000), inventor of the five-figure summary and boxplot

John Tukey was a prominent and prolific US statistician, based at Princeton University and Bell Laboratories. As well as working in some very technical areas, he was a great promoter of simple ways of picturing and summarising data, and invented both the five-figure summary and the boxplot (except that he called them the 'five-number summary' and the 'box-and-whisker plot').

He had what has been described as an 'unusual' lecturing style. The statistician Peter McCullagh describes a lecture he gave at Imperial College, London in 1977:

> Tukey ambled to the podium, a great bear of a man dressed in baggy pants and a black knitted shirt. These might once have been a matching pair, but the vintage was such that it was hard to tell. ... The words came ..., not many, like overweight parcels, delivered at a slow unfaltering pace. ... Tukey turned to face the audience .... 'Comments, queries, suggestions?' he asked .... As he waited for a response, he clambered onto the podium and manoeuvred until he was sitting cross-legged facing the audience. ... We in the audience sat like spectators at the zoo waiting for the great bear to move or say something. But the great bear appeared to be doing the same thing, and the feeling was not comfortable. ... After a long while, ... he extracted from his pocket a bag of dried prunes and proceeded to eat them in silence, one by one. The war of nerves continued ... four prunes, five prunes. ... How many prunes would it take to end the silence?

(Source: McCullagh, P. (2003) 'John Wilder Tukey', *Biographical Memoirs of Fellows of the Royal Society*, vol. 49, pp. 537–555.)

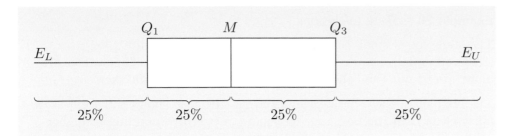

Figure 18 A standard boxplot with annotation

A typical boxplot looks something like Figure 18 because in most batches of data the values are more densely packed in the middle of the batch and are less densely packed in the extremes. This means that each whisker is usually longer than half the length of the box. This is illustrated again in the next example.

Example 19 *Boxplot for the prices of small televisions*

The boxplot for the batch of 20 television prices (last worked with in Example 18) is shown in Figure 19.

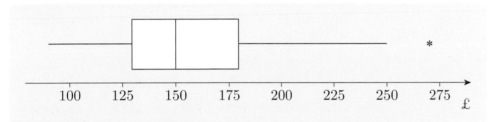

Figure 19 Boxplot of batch of 20 television prices

You can see that each whisker is longer than half the length of the box.

However, this boxplot has a new feature. The whisker on the left goes right down to the lower extreme. But the whisker on the right does not go right to the upper extreme. The highest extreme data value, 270, which might potentially be regarded as an outlier, is marked separately with a star. Then the whisker extends only to cover the data values that are not extreme enough to be regarded as potential outliers. The highest of these values is 250.

In Unit 3, you will learn in detail how to draw a boxplot. This includes a rule to decide which data values (if any) can be regarded as potential outliers that are plotted separately on the diagram.

Example 19 is the subject of Screencast 4 for Unit 2 (see the module website).

One important use of boxplots is to picture and describe the overall shape of a batch of data.

Use of boxplots will also be covered in Unit 3.

Skewness and symmetry were
discussed in Subsection 5.2 of
Unit 1.

Example 20   *Skew televisions*

The stemplot of small television prices, last seen in Figure 13
(Subsection 3.2), shows a lack of symmetry. Since the higher values are
more spread out than the lower values, the data are right-skew.

The boxplot of these data, given in Figure 19, also shows this right-skew
fairly clearly. In the box, the *right*-hand part (corresponding to higher
prices) is rather longer than the left-hand part, and the *right*-hand whisker
is longer than the left-hand whisker.

Activity 13   *Skew gas prices?*

A stemplot of the gas price data from Activity 2 (Subsection 1.2) is shown,
yet again, in Figure 20.

$$
\begin{array}{r|l}
374 & 0\ 0\ 3 \\
375 & \\
376 & 0\ 7 \\
377 & 6 \\
378 & 4 \\
379 & 5\ 6 \\
380 & 1\ 1\ 4\ 5 \\
381 & 8 \\
\end{array}
$$

$n = 14$ $374 \,|\, 0$ represents 3.740p per kWh

Figure 20   Stemplot of 14 gas prices

(a) Prepare a five-figure summary of the batch.

(b) Figure 21 shows the boxplot of these data that you have already seen
in Figure 17. What do the stemplot and boxplot tell us about the
symmetry and/or skewness of the batch?

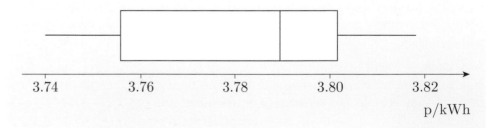

Figure 21   Boxplot of batch of 14 gas prices

Example 21   *Camera prices: skew or not?*

In Example 20 and Activity 13 you saw how boxplots look for batches of data that are right-skew or left-skew. What happens in a batch that is more symmetrical?

For the small batch of camera prices from Table 2 (Subsection 1.2), a (stretched) stemplot is shown in Figure 22.

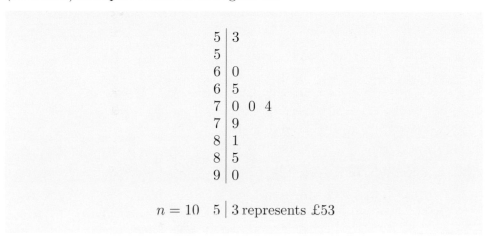

$$
\begin{array}{c|ccc}
5 & 3 \\
5 & \\
6 & 0 \\
6 & 5 \\
7 & 0 \ 0 \ 4 \\
7 & 9 \\
8 & 1 \\
8 & 5 \\
9 & 0 \\
\end{array}
$$

$n = 10$ $5 \mid 3$ represents £53

Figure 22   Stemplot of ten camera prices

The stemplot looks reasonably symmetric.

A boxplot of the data, Figure 23, confirms the impression of symmetry. The two parts of the box are roughly equal in length, and the two whiskers are also roughly equal in length.

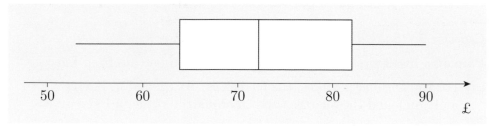

Figure 23   Boxplot of batch of ten camera prices

You have now spent quite a lot of time looking at various ways of investigating prices and, in particular, at methods of measuring the location and spread of the prices of particular commodities.

In order to begin to answer our question, *Are people getting better or worse off?*, we need to know not just location (and spread) of prices but also how these prices are *changing* from year to year. That is the subject of the rest of this unit.

Exercises on Section 3

Exercise 6　*Finding quartiles and the interquartile range*

(a) For the arithmetic scores in Exercise 1 (Section 1), find the quartiles and calculate the interquartile range. The stemplot of the scores is given below.

```
 0 | 7
 1 | 5
 2 |
 3 | 3 5
 4 | 2 2 3
 5 | 5 8
 6 | 4 6 8
 7 | 1 1 6 8 9
 8 | 0 1 1 3 4 5 5 6 9
 9 | 1 1 3 5 9
10 | 0 0
```

$n = 33$　$0 \mid 7$ represents a score of 7%

(b) For the television prices in Exercise 1, find the quartiles and calculate the interquartile range. The table of prices is given below.

170	180	190	200	220	229	230	230	230
230	250	269	269	270	279	299	300	300
315	320	349	350	400	429	649	699	

Exercise 7　*Some five-figure summaries*

Prepare a five-figure summary for each of the two batches from Exercise 1.

(a) For the arithmetic scores, the median is 79% (found in Exercise 1), and you found the quartiles and interquartile range in Exercise 6.

(b) For the television prices, the median is £270 (found in Exercise 1), and you found the quartiles and interquartile range in Exercise 6.

Exercise 8   *Boxplots and the shape of distributions*

Boxplots of the two batches used in Exercises 1, 6 and 7 are shown in Figures 24 and 25. On the basis of these diagrams, comment on the symmetry and/or skewness of these data.

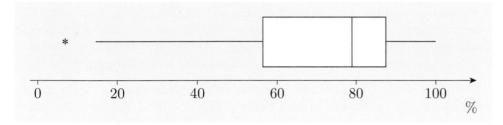

Figure 24   Boxplot of batch of 33 arithmetic scores

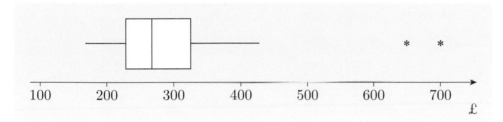

Figure 25   Boxplot of batch of 26 television prices

4 A simple chained price index

You have already seen that it is not a simple task to measure the price of even a *single* commodity at a *fixed* time and place. Measuring the change in price of a single commodity from one year to the next will be even more complicated but, as was said in Subsection 1.1, to answer our question it is necessary to measure the *changes* in the prices of the *whole range* of goods and services which people use. Moreover, since we wish to know how all the different changes in the prices of these goods and services affect people, we need to take into account those people's consumption patterns. For example, a large increase in the price of high-quality caviar will not affect most people's budgets since most households' shopping lists do not include this commodity!

This makes the task of measuring price changes and examining how they affect us seem exceedingly difficult; but such a task is carried out in the UK regularly each month, organised by the Office for National Statistics.

(Most of the prices are actually collected by a market research company under contract to the Office for National Statistics.) The results of their data collection and subsequent calculations are summarised in two measures called the Consumer Prices Index (CPI) and the Retail Prices Index (RPI).

'Indices' is the plural of 'index'

These indices do not measure prices. Each is an index of price *changes* over time, and one or both of these indices are commonly used when people make comparisons about the cost of living. As you will see in Unit 3, they are highly relevant measures for those engaged in wage bargaining.

The RPI and the CPI are both 'chained' in the sense that the index value for each year is linked to the year before. The very first link in the chain is called the *base year* and it is given an index value of 100.

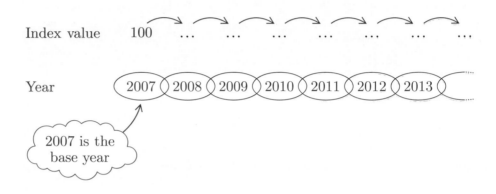

Index value   100   ...   .

Year   2007 2008 2009 2010 2011 2012 2013

2007 is the base year

Figure 26   A chained index

4.1   A two-commodity price index

Section 5 includes an outline of how the information used to calculate the official UK price indices is collected, and describes how the indices are calculated. To introduce ideas, in this section we describe a very much simpler example of a price index calculation. It uses exactly the same basic method of calculation as the actual Retail Prices Index. (Not every index is calculated in this way, as you will see in Unit 3 with the Average Weekly Earnings statistic.)

The context is a mythical computing company, Gradgrind Ltd, whose organisation and exploits will be used occasionally in this and later units to illustrate various points.

Gradgrind Ltd uses both gas and electricity in its operations. Table 7 shows the price they paid for each fuel in 2007 and 2008. The prices are shown in £ per megawatt hour (MWh). (It is more usual, in the UK, for prices to be quoted in pence per kilowatt hour (p/kWh). Here, £/MWh have been used simply to make some of the later calculations a little more straightforward. Because there are 100 pence in £1 and 1000 kilowatts in a

The original Mr. Gradgrind, from an 1870s illustration to Charles Dickens' *Hard Times*, first published in 1854. Dickens had Gradgrind describe himself as, 'A man of realities. A man of facts and calculations.' But don't let that put you off.

megawatt, £10/MWh is exactly the same price as 1p/kWh – so Gradgrind's gas price in 2007, for instance, was 2.4p/kWh.)

Table 7   Gradgrind's energy prices in 2007 and 2008

	2007	2008
Gas (£/MWh)	24	29
Electricity (£/MWh)	76	87

If we were interested in looking at the change in price of just *one* of these fuels, say gas, things would be relatively straightforward. For instance, it might well be appropriate to look at the increase in price as a percentage of the price in 2007.

Activity 14   *Gradgrind's gas price increase*

Work out the increase in Gradgrind's gas price between 2007 and 2008 as a percentage of the 2007 price.

So we could say that, for this company at least, gas has gone up by 20.8%. In other words, for every £1 they spent on gas in 2007, they would have spent £1.208 in 2008 if they had bought the same amount of gas in each year. Or putting it another way, for every 100 units of money (pence, pounds, whatever) they spent in 2007, they would have spent 120.8 units of money in 2008 if they had bought the same amount. So a way of representing this price change would have been to define an *index* for the gas price such that it takes the value 100 for 2007, and 120.8 for 2008.

Notice that the value of the gas price index for 2008 could be calculated as

$$(\text{value of the index in 2007, which is taken as } 100) \times \frac{\text{gas price in 2008}}{\text{gas price in 2007}}.$$

That is, the value of the index in one year is the value of the index in the previous year multiplied by a *price ratio*, in this case the *gas price ratio for 2008 relative to 2007*. This ratio, as a number, is 1.208.

But Gradgrind did not only use gas, they used electricity as well, and the aim here is to find a representation of their overall fuel price change, not just the change in gas prices.

An *electricity price ratio for 2008 relative to 2007* can be worked out, like the gas price ratio. It is $\frac{87}{76} \simeq 1.145$.

Activity 15   *Gradgrind's electricity price index*

Use the electricity price ratio above to find the increase in Gradgrind's electricity price between 2007 and 2008 as a percentage of the 2007 price. What would the 2008 value be for a price index of Gradgrind's electricity price alone, calculated in the same way as the gas price index (with 2007 as the base year)?

But this has got us no further in finding a price index that simultaneously covers *both* fuels.

One possibility might be to look at how Gradgrind's total expenditure on these two fuels changed from 2007 to 2008. The expenditures are given in Table 8.

Table 8   Gradgrind's energy expenditure (£) in 2007 and 2008

	2007	2008
Gas	9 298	8 145
Electricity	3 205	2 991
Total	12 503	11 136

This seems not to have helped. The total expenditure went down, but you have already seen that the prices of both gas and electricity went up.

Activity 16   *How much fuel did Gradgrind use?*

Use the data in Tables 7 and 8 to find the quantity of each fuel that Gradgrind used in 2007 and 2008 (in MWh). Hence explain why the energy expenditure fell.

Remember the aim is to produce a measure of price *changes*. So looking at expenditure changes does not do the right thing, since expenditure depends on the amount of fuel consumed as well as the price.

One possibility might be as follows. We could work out how much Gradgrind *would have* spent on fuel in 2008 if the consumptions of both fuels had not changed from 2007. That would remove the effect of any changes in consumption. Then we could calculate an overall energy price ratio for 2008 relative to 2007 by dividing the total expenditure on energy for 2008 (using the 2007 consumption figures) by the total expenditure on energy for 2007 (again using the 2007 consumption figures).

You should have found, in Activity 16, that the quantities of gas and electricity consumed in 2007 were, respectively, 387.4 MWh and 42.2 MWh. To buy those quantities at 2008 prices would have cost (in £): $29 \times 387.4 = 11\,234.6$ for the gas and $87 \times 42.2 = 3671.4$ for the electricity, giving a total expenditure of

$$£(11\,234.6 + 3671.4) = £14\,906.0.$$

So a reasonable overall energy price ratio for 2008 relative to 2007 can be found by dividing this total by the 2007 total expenditure, again calculated using the 2007 consumptions. The appropriate figure for 2007 is just the actual total expenditure, which (in £) was $9298 + 3205 = 12\,503$ (see Table 8). This gives an overall energy price ratio for 2008 relative to 2007 as

$$\frac{14\,906.0}{12\,503} \simeq 1.192.$$

Now we have an appropriate price ratio, the Gradgrind energy price index can be set as 100 for the base year, 2007, and the value of the 2008 index is found by multiplying the 2007 index value by the price ratio:

2008 index $= 100 \times 1.192 = 119.2$.

This is indeed how a chained index of this kind is calculated – but the calculations are rather messy. You might be wondering whether it would be simpler to calculate the overall energy price ratio as a weighted mean of the two price ratios for the two fuels, in much the same way that weighted means were used to combine prices in Section 2. If you did think this, you would be right – and furthermore, the resulting overall energy price ratio is exactly the same as has just been found, if we make the right choice of weights. The overall energy price ratio for 2008 relative to 2007 is just a weighted mean of the two price ratios for gas and electricity, with the 2007 expenditures as weights.

Just to show it really does come to the same thing, let us see how it works with the numbers, using the formula for weighted means in Subsection 2.3.

	Price ratio (2008 relative to 2007) x	Weight (2007 expenditure) w
Gas	1.208	9298
Electricity	1.145	3205

The weighted average of these price ratios is

$$\frac{(1.208 \times 9298) + (1.145 \times 3205)}{9298 + 3205} = \frac{14\,901.709}{12\,503} \simeq 1.192,$$

giving the same value for the overall energy price ratio for 2008 relative to 2007 as we found earlier. (And this is not some sort of fluke that applies only to these particular numbers; it can be shown mathematically that it always works.)

Activity 17   Gradgrind's energy price ratio for 2009 relative to 2008

Table 9   Gradgrind's energy prices and expenditures for 2008 and 2009

	2008	2009
Gas price (£/MWh)	29	30
Gas expenditure (£)	8 145	23 733
Electricity price (£/MWh)	87	98
Electricity expenditure (£)	2 991	2 275

(a) Using the data in Table 9, calculate the price ratios for gas and for electricity, in each case for 2009 relative to 2008.

(b) With the 2008 expenditures as weights, use your answers to part (a) to calculate the overall energy price ratio for 2009 relative to 2008.

(c) Now see what happens if you use the 2009 expenditures as weights to calculate the overall energy price ratio for 2009 relative to 2008. How do the results of the calculation differ from what you got in part (b)?

The reason that the price ratios you calculated in parts (b) and (c) in Activity 17 were so different is that Gradgrind's 'energy mix' changed a lot over the year. Compared with 2008, in 2009 they spent a great deal more on gas but less on electricity. The weighted mean of the gas and electricity price ratios is, in both cases, nearer the price ratio for gas than that for electricity – this is Rule 2 for weighted means – but it is even nearer the gas weighted mean when the 2009 expenditures are used. This is because the weight for gas is proportionally much greater than it is when the 2008 expenditures are used as weights.

This all shows that it *does* make a difference which expenditures are used as weights. In practice, it is much more common to use the expenditures from the earlier year – 2008 in this case – as weights. In some circumstances, though, there are good reasons for using the later year, or indeed some more complicated set of weights that depend on both expenditures. However, in this unit we shall use the expenditures from the earlier year to provide the weights, partly because that matches more closely what is done in calculating the official UK price indices.

Another possibility for weights would have been to continue to use the 2007 expenditures. These were used to find the overall energy price ratio for 2008 relative to 2007 and could be used for later years as well. Again, in some circumstances this would make sense, but here the pattern of Gradgrind's fuel expenditure has changed a lot over time, and weights should change in consequence. To continue to use the 2007 expenditures for all later years would mean that this change in the relative importance to Gradgrind of the two fuels would never be taken into account. Instead, to obtain the overall energy price ratio from one year to the next, we use the fuel expenditures in the earlier year as weights, so each year the weights change.

That determines the choice of weights in forming an overall price ratio. Now, how is that used to find the energy price *index*? Here we simply continue the 'chaining' that started when finding the 2008 index: the 2009 index is found by multiplying the value of the index for the previous year, 2008, by the overall energy price ratio for 2009 relative to 2008. The value of the index for 2008 was calculated earlier as 119.2, and (using the weights from the previous year) the overall energy price ratio for 2009 relative to 2008 was found in Activity 17(b) as 1.059. So the value of Gradgrind's energy price index for 2009 is

$$119.2 \times 1.059 \simeq 126.2.$$

(So, in a particular kind of average way, Gradgrind's energy prices for 2009 have risen by 26.2% since the base year, 2007.)

In general, the value index for a particular year is found by multiplying the value of the index for the previous year by the overall energy price ratio for that year relative to the previous year. This is illustrated in Figure 27.

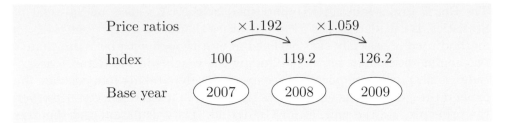

Figure 27   Determining a chained price index

In the process of *chaining*, the overall price ratio is calculated anew each year, looking back only at the previous year. The ratio is used to 'chain' to earlier years and hence determine the value of the index. This method of calculating a **chained price index** is summarised below. Although there were only two commodities (gas and electricity) in Gradgrind's index, this summary is not restricted to two commodities.

Procedure used to calculate a chained price index

1.   For each year calculate the following.

*   The **price ratio** for each commodity covered by the index:

$$\frac{\text{price that year}}{\text{price previous year}}.$$

*   The weighted mean of all these price ratios, using as weights the expenditure on each commodity in the previous year. This weighted mean is called the **all-commodities price ratio**.

2.   For each year, the value of the index is

value of index for previous year × all-commodities price ratio.

The value of the index in the first year is set at 100; this date is the **base date** of the index.

Activity 18   *Gradgrind's energy price index for 2010*

Use the data in Table 10, and other necessary numbers from previous calculations, to calculate the value of Gradgrind's energy price index for 2010.

Table 10   Gradgrind's energy prices and expenditures for 2009 and 2010

	2009	2010
Gas price (£/MWh)	30	28
Gas expenditure (£)	23 733	23 969
Electricity price (£/MWh)	98	88
Electricity expenditure (£)	2 275	2 920

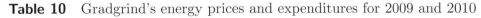

The Retail Prices Index (RPI), published by the UK Office for National Statistics, is calculated once a month rather than once a year, but the method used is basically that outlined above, though with far more than two commodities. The process of finding the weights in the Retail Prices Index is also more complicated, because it involves taking into account the expenditures of millions of people as measured in a major survey. However, the principles are the same as for Gradgrind. The calculation each January follows exactly this method. In the other 11 months of the year, the calculation is very similar but uses only the increases in prices since the previous January. In the next section, you will learn more about how all this works.

See Subsection 5.2 for the details of these calculations.

Exercise on Section 4

Exercise 9   *Gradgrind's energy price index for 2011*

Use the data in Table 11, and the fact that Gradgrind's energy price index for 2010 was 117.4 (as found in Activity 18), to calculate the value of Gradgrind's energy price index for 2011.

Table 11   Gradgrind's energy prices and expenditures for 2010 and 2011

	2010	2011
Gas price (£/MWh)	28	30
Gas expenditure (£)	23 969	24 282
Electricity price (£/MWh)	88	86
Electricity expenditure (£)	2 920	3 117

5   The UK government price indices

'The huge squeeze on Brits was laid bare today as figures showed inflation has soared to a 20-year high.' (*The Sun*, 18 October 2011)

'Overall, prices in the economy rose 0.6% on the month from August.' (*Guardian*, 18 October 2011)

'Inflation in the UK continued to fall in February, thanks largely to lower gas and electricity bills.' (BBC News website, 20 March 2012)

'UK inflation rises more than expected.' (*Daily Telegraph*, 16 August 2011)

How often have you read or heard statements like these in the media? Have you ever wondered how 'inflation' is measured, or precisely what is meant by a statement such as 'prices rose by 0.6%'? In Subsection 5.3, you will see that 'rates of inflation' are often calculated in the UK using an index of prices paid by consumers, the Consumer Prices Index (CPI), or another slightly different index, the Retail Prices Index (RPI). These indices may be used to calculate the percentage by which prices in general have risen over any given period, and (roughly speaking) this is what is meant by inflation. But what exactly do these price indices measure, and how are they calculated? These are the questions that are addressed in this section.

5.1   What are the CPI and RPI?

The CPI and the RPI are the main measures used in the UK to record changes in the level of the prices most people pay for the goods and services they buy. The RPI is intended to reflect the average spending pattern of the great majority of private households. Only two classes of private households are excluded, on the grounds that their spending patterns differ greatly from those of the others: pensioner households and high-income households. The CPI, however, has a wider remit – it is intended to reflect the spending of *all* UK residents, and also covers some costs incurred by foreign visitors to the UK.

The CPI and RPI are calculated in a similar way to the price index for Gradgrind Ltd's energy in Section 4. However, they are calculated once a month rather than just once a year, and are based on a very large '**basket of goods**'. The contents of the basket and the weights assigned to the items in the basket are updated annually to reflect changes in spending patterns (as was the case with Gradgrind's index for energy prices), and the index is 'chained' to previous values. However, once decided on at the beginning of the year, the contents of the basket and their weights remain fixed throughout the year.

For the RPI, the price ratio for the basket each month is calculated relative to the previous January. Then the value of the index is obtained by multiplying the value of the index for the previous January by this price ratio. For example,

RPI for Nov. 2011 = RPI for Jan. 2011

× (price ratio for Nov. 2011 relative to Jan. 2011).

The CPI works in much the same way, except that price ratios are calculated relative to the previous December. So, for example,

CPI for Nov. 2011 = CPI for Dec. 2010

× (price ratio for Nov. 2011 relative to Dec. 2010).

Since these price indices are calculated from price ratios, they measure price changes in terms of the *ratio* of the overall level of prices in a given month to the overall level of prices at an earlier date. In practice, data on most prices are collected on a particular day near the middle of the month; the values of the RPI and CPI calculated using these data are referred to simply as the values of the RPI and CPI for the month. For example, the RPI took the value 239.9 in February 2012. This value measures the ratio of the overall level of prices in February 2012 to the overall level of prices on a date at which the index was fixed at its starting value of 100. This date, called a *base date*, is 13 January 1987 (at the time of writing). Thus the general level of prices in February 2012, as measured by the RPI, was $239.9/100 = 2.399$ times the general level of prices in January 1987.

The base date has *no* significance other than to act as a reference point. (The CPI base date is 2005 and this refers to the average level of prices throughout 2005, not to a specific date in 2005.)

The RPI and CPI are each based on a very large 'basket' of goods and services. (The two baskets are similar, but not exactly the same.) Each contains around 700 items including most of the usual things people buy: food, clothes, fuel, household goods, housing, transport, services, and so on. Each basket is an 'average' basket for a broad range of households. The items in the baskets are often grouped into broader categories. For the RPI, the five fundamental groups are: 'Food and catering', 'Alcohol and tobacco', 'Housing and household expenditure', 'Personal expenditure' and 'Travel and leisure'. These groups are divided into 14 more detailed *subgroups* (which are further divided into *sections*), as shown in Figure 28.

The items in the CPI basket are divided into 12 broad groupings called *divisions*, which are further subdivided.

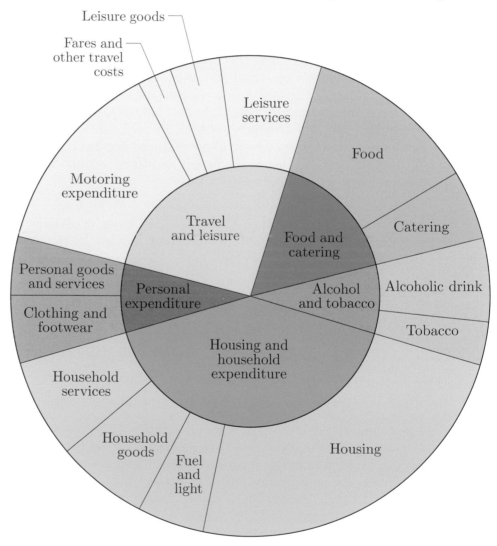

Figure 28   Structure of the RPI in 2012 (based on data from the Office for National Statistics)

The inner circle shows the five groups, and the outer ring shows the 14 subgroups. Notice that in the inner circle the sector labelled 'Food and catering' has been drawn almost twice as large (as measured by area) as that labelled 'Alcohol and tobacco'. This reflects the fact that the typical household spends nearly twice as much on food and catering as on alcohol and tobacco. The weight of an item or group reflects how much money is spent on it. So the weight of the 'Food and catering' group is almost twice that of 'Alcohol and tobacco'.

The outer ring represents the same total expenditure as the inner circle, but in more detail. For example, in the outer ring the area labelled 'Food' (which mostly consists of food bought for use in the home) is more than twice as large as that labelled 'Catering' (which includes meals in restaurants and canteens, and take-away meals and snacks), reflecting the fact that the typical household spends more than twice as much on food as on catering; the weight of the subgroup 'Food' is more than double the weight of the subgroup 'Catering'. The chart gives a good indication of average spending patterns in the UK in the early 21st century.

Activity 19   *The expenditure of a typical household*

(a) Using Figure 28, estimate roughly what fraction of the expenditure of a typical household is on each of the following groups and subgroups:

- Personal expenditure

- Housing and household expenditure

- Housing

(b) Suppose that a household spends a total of £540 per week on goods and services that are covered by the RPI. Use your answers to part (a) to estimate very approximately how much is spent each week on each of the groups and subgroups in part (a).

To ensure that the basket of goods for the index reflects the proportion of average spending devoted to different types of goods and services, it is necessary to find out how people actually spend their money. The Living Costs and Food Survey (LCF) records the spending reported by a sample of 5000 households spread throughout the UK. Data from the LCF are used to calculate the weights of most of the items included in the RPI basket. Since 1962, the weights have been revised each year, so that the index is always based on a basket of goods and services that is as up to date as possible. Because of this regular weight revision, the index is chained (as was the Gradgrind Ltd index).

(Most of the weights for the CPI come from a different source, the UK National Accounts, though in turn this source is partly based on data from the LCF. Again, the weights are revised each year.)

The weight of a group or subgroup directly depends on the average expenditure of households on that item. In Subsection 2.1, you saw that it is only the *relative* size of the weights that affects the value of the weighted mean – this is Rule 1 for weighted means. So instead of using the average expenditure of an item as its weight, the expenditure figures for the items can all be multiplied by the same factor to produce a new, more convenient, set of weights. For the RPI, this factor is chosen so that the sum of the weights is 1000. Table 12 shows the 2012 weights used in the RPI for the groups and subgroups. Notice that each group weight is obtained by summing the weights for its subgroups.

Table 12 2012 RPI weights

Group	Subgroup	Weight	Group weight
Food and catering	Food	114	
	Catering	47	161
Alcohol and tobacco	Alcoholic drink	56	
	Tobacco	29	85
Housing and household expenditure	Housing	237	
	Fuel and light	46	
	Household goods	62	
	Household services	67	412
Personal expenditure	Clothing and footwear	45	
	Personal goods and services	39	84
Travel and leisure	Motoring expenditure	131	
	Fares and other travel costs	23	
	Leisure goods	33	
	Leisure services	71	258
All items (i.e. the sum of the weights)			1000

The following checklist provided contains the major categories of goods and services included in the RPI. In the next activity, you will be asked to complete the last three columns of this checklist to make rough estimates of your household's group weights.

A checklist for one household's average monthly expenditure

	Expenditure and weights			Your expenditure and weights		
	Expenditure 2012 (£)	Group totals (£)	Group weights	Expenditure 2012 (£)	Group totals (£)	Group weights
Food and catering						
– at home	370					
– canteens, snacks and take-aways	80					
– restaurant meals	20					
		470	266		_____	_____
Alcohol and tobacco						
– alcoholic drink	8					
– cigarettes and tobacco	0					
		8	5		_____	_____
Housing and household expenditure						
– mortgage interest/rent	82					
– council tax	95					
water charges	47					
– house insurance	29					
– repairs/maintenance/DIY	40					
– gas/electricity/coal/oil bills	210					
– household goods (furniture appliances, consumables, etc.)	70					
– telephone and internet bills	20					
– school and university fees	0					
– pet care	0					
		593	336		_____	_____
Personal expenditure						
– clothing and footwear	45					
– other (hairdressing, chemists' goods, etc.)	10					
		55	31		_____	_____
Travel and leisure						
– motoring (purchase, maintenance, petrol, tax, insurance)	210					
– fares	200					
– books, newspapers, magazines	80					
– audio-visual equipment, CDs, etc.	15					
– toys, photographic and sports goods	3					
– TV purchase/rental, licence	0					
– cinema, theatre, etc.	30					
– holidays	100					
		638	362		_____	_____
		1764	1000		_____	_____

The figures already in the checklist were completed for a two-person household. Some of the figures were accurate, others were necessarily very rough estimates. Nevertheless, the household's weights give a reasonable indication of the proportion of the household's expenditure (in 2012) on the five main groups used in the RPI.

The total expenditure was £1764. So the group weights were calculated by multiplying all the group total expenditures by a constant factor of 1000/1764, to ensure the weights sum to 1000. The weight for 'Food and catering', for example, is

$$470 \times \frac{1000}{1764} \simeq 266.$$

Another way to calculate this is to multiply the proportion of monthly expenditure spent on food and catering by 1000. The proportion is

$$\frac{470}{1764} \simeq 0.266.$$

Since the total weight is 1000, the weight for 'Food and catering' is

$$0.266 \times 1000 = 266.$$

Notice that the group weights for this particular household differ quite considerably from those used in the RPI in 2012 (see Table 12). For instance, a much greater proportion of expenditure is on 'Food and catering' and a much smaller proportion is spent on 'Alcohol and tobacco'.

Activity 20   *Your own household's expenditure*

Make rough estimates of your own household's expenditure last year and complete the final columns of the checklist above. For some categories, you may find it easier just to make a rough estimate of, say, your annual expenditure and then divide by 12. If you have no idea at all for a category, then use the corresponding figure in the checklist as a starting point for your own expenditure and adjust it up or down depending on how you think you spend your money. One way of checking that your figures are sensible is to consider how the sum of the expenditures relates to your household's monthly income. Do not spend more than 15 minutes on estimating your expenditure; accurate figures are not needed.

Divide each group expenditure by your monthly expenditure total and then multiply by 1000 to calculate your household's group weights.

How do your household's weights compare with those used in the RPI in 2012?

5.2 Calculating the price indices

This subsection concentrates on how the RPI is calculated. Generally the CPI is calculated in a similar way, though some of the details differ. To measure price changes in general, it is sufficient to select a limited number of representative items to indicate the price movements of a broad range of similar items. For each section of the RPI, a number of *representative items* are selected for pricing. The selection is made at the beginning of the year and remains the same throughout the year. It is designed in such a way that the price movements of the representative items, when combined using a weighted mean, provide a good estimate of price movements in the section as a whole.

For example, in 2012 the representative items in the 'Bread' section (which is contained in the 'Food and catering' group) were: large white sliced loaf, large white unsliced loaf, large wholemeal loaf, bread rolls, garlic bread. Changes in the prices of these types of bread are assumed to be representative of changes in bread prices as a whole. Note that although the *price ratio* for bread is based on this sample of five types of bread, the calculation of the appropriate *weight* for bread is based on *all* kinds of bread. This weight is calculated using data collected in the Living Costs and Food Survey.

Collecting the data

The bulk of the data on price changes required to calculate the RPI is collected by staff of a market research company and forwarded to the Office for National Statistics for processing. Collecting the prices is a major operation: well over 100 000 prices are collected each month for around 560 different items. The prices being charged at a large range of shops and other outlets throughout the UK are mostly recorded on a predetermined Tuesday near the middle of the month. Prices for the remaining items, about 140 of them, are obtained from central sources because, for example, the prices of some items do not vary from one place to another.

One aim of the RPI is to make it possible to compare prices in any two months, and this involves calculating a value of the price index itself for every month.

Changing the representative items

The Office for National Statistics (ONS) updates the basket of goods every year, reflecting advancing technology, changing tastes and consumers' spending habits. The media often have fun writing about the way the list of representative items changes each year.

In the 1950s, the mangle, crisps and dance hall admissions were added to the basket, with soap flakes among the items taken out.

Two decades later, the cassette recorder and dried mashed potato made it in, with prunes being excluded.

Then after the turn of the century, mobile phone handsets and fruit smoothies were included. The old fashioned staples of an evening at home – gin and slippers – were removed from the basket.

So now, in 2012, it is the turn of tablet computers to be added to mark the growing popularity of this type of technology.

That received the most coverage when it was added to the basket of goods, with the ONS highlighting this digital-age addition in its media releases.

But those seafaring captains who once used the then unusual fruit as a symbol to show they were home and hosting might be astonished to find that centuries on, the pineapple has also been added to the inflation basket.

Technically, the pineapple has been added to give more varied coverage in the basket of fruit and vegetables, the prices of which can be volatile.

(Source: BBC News website, 14 March 2012)

So, calculating the RPI involves two kinds of data:

* the price data, collected every month
* the weights, representing expenditure patterns, updated once a year.

Once the price data have been collected each month, various checks, such as looking for unbelievable prices, are applied and corrections made if necessary. Checking data for obvious errors is an important part of any data analysis.

Then an averaging process is used to obtain a price ratio for each item that fairly reflects how the price of the item has changed across the country. The exact details are quite complicated and are not described here. (If you want more details, they are given in the *Consumer Price Indices Technical Manual*, available from the ONS website. *Consumer Price Indices: A brief guide* is also available from the same website.)

For each item, a price ratio is calculated that compares its price with the previous January. For instance, for November 2011, the resulting price ratio for an item is an average value of

$$\frac{\text{price in November 2011}}{\text{price in January 2011}}.$$

The next steps in the process combine these price ratios, using weighted means, to obtain 14 subgroup price ratios, and then the group price ratios for the five groups. Finally, the group price ratios are combined to give the **all-item price ratio**. This is the price ratio, relative to the previous January, for the 'basket' of goods and services as a whole that make up the RPI.

The all-item price ratio tells us how, on average, the RPI 'basket' compares in price with the previous January. The value of the RPI for a given month is found by the method described in Section 4, that is, by multiplying the value of the RPI for the previous January by the all-item price ratio for that month (relative to the previous January):

RPI for month x = (RPI for previous January)

$\times$ (all-item price ratio for month x)

Thus, to calculate the RPI for November 2011, the final step is to multiply the value of the RPI in January 2011 by the all-item price ratio for November 2011.

Example 22 *Calculating the RPI for November 2011*

Here are the details of the last two stages of calculation of the RPI for November 2011, after the group price ratios have been calculated, relative to January 2011. The appropriate data are in Table 13.

Table 13 Calculating the all-item price ratio for November 2011

Group	Price ratio r	Weight w	Ratio × weight rw
Food and catering	1.030	165	169.950
Alcohol and tobacco	1.050	88	92.400
Housing and household expenditure	1.037	408	423.096
Personal expenditure	1.128	82	92.496
Travel and leisure	1.026	257	263.682
Sum		1000	1041.624

(Source: Office for National Statistics)

You may have noticed that the weights here do not exactly match those in Table 12. That is because the weights here are the 2011 weights, and those in Table 12 are the 2012 weights, and as has been explained, the weights are revised each year.

The all-item price ratio is a weighted average of the group price ratios given in the table. If the price ratios are denoted by the letter r, and the weights by w, then the weighted mean of the price ratios is the sum of the five values of rw divided by the sum of the five values of w. The formula, from Subsection 2.3, is

$$\text{all-item price ratio} = \frac{\text{sum of products (price ratio} \times \text{weight)}}{\text{sum of weights}}$$

$$= \frac{\sum rw}{\sum w}.$$

The sums are given in Table 13. (The sum of the weights is 1000, because the RPI weights are chosen to add up to 1000.) Although Table 13 gives the individual rw values, there is no need for you to write down these individual products when finding a weighted mean (unless you are asked to do so). As mentioned previously, your calculator may enable you to calculate the weighted mean directly, or you may use its memory to store a running total of rw.

Now the all-item price ratio for November 2011 (relative to January 2011) can be calculated as

$$\frac{1041.624}{1000} = 1.041\,624.$$

This tells us that, on average, the RPI basket of goods cost $1.041\,624$ times as much in November 2011 as in January 2011.

The published value of the RPI for January 2011 was 229.0. So, using the formula,

$$\text{RPI for Nov. 2011} = \text{RPI for Jan. 2011}$$
$$\times \text{(all-item price ratio for Nov. 2011)}$$
$$= 229.0 \times 1.041\,624$$
$$= 238.531\,896 \simeq 238.5.$$

The final result has been rounded to one decimal place because actual published RPI figures are rounded to one decimal place.

Example 22 is the subject of Screencast 5 for Unit 2 (see the module website).

The same 2011 weights were used to calculate the RPI for every month from February 2011 to January 2012 inclusive. For each of these months, the price ratios were calculated relative to January 2011, and the RPI was finally calculated by multiplying the RPI for January 2011 by the all-item price ratio for the month in question. In February 2012, however, the process began again (as it does every February). A new set of weights, the 2012 weights, came into use. Price ratios were calculated relative to January 2012, and the RPI was found by multiplying the RPI value for January 2012 by the all-item price ratio. This procedure was used until January 2013, and so on.

The process of calculating the RPI can be summarised as follows.

Calculating the RPI

1. The data used are prices, collected monthly, and weights, based on the Living Costs and Food Survey, updated annually.

2. Each month, for each item, a price ratio is calculated, which gives the price of the item that month divided by its price the previous January.

3. Group price ratios are calculated from the price ratios using weighted means.

4. Weighted means are then used to calculate the all-item price ratio. Denoting the group price ratios by r and the group weights by w, the all-item price ratio is

$$\frac{\sum rw}{\sum w}.$$

5. The value of the RPI for that month is found by multiplying the value of the RPI for the previous January by the all-item price ratio:

RPI for month x = RPI for previous January

$\times$ (all-item price ratio for month x).

The weights for a particular year are used in calculating the RPI for every month from February of that year to January of the following year.

Activity 21   *Calculating the RPI for July 2011*

Find the value of the RPI in July 2011 by completing the following table and the formulas below. The value of the RPI in January 2011 was 229.0. (The base date was January 1987.)

Table 14   Calculating the RPI for July 2011

Group	Price ratio for July 2011 relative to January 2011 r	2011 weights w	Price ratio × weight rw
Food and catering	1.024	165	
Alcohol and tobacco	1.042	88	
Housing and household expenditure	1.012	408	
Personal expenditure	1.053	82	
Travel and leisure	1.030	257	
Sum			

(Source: Office for National Statistics)

sum $(w) =$, sum of products $(rw) =$,

all-item price ratio $= \dfrac{\text{sum of products }(rw)}{\text{sum}(w)} =$, value of RPI in July 2011 =   .

The published value for the RPI in July 2011 was 234.7, slightly different from the value you should have obtained in Activity 21 (that is, 234.6). The discrepancy arises because the government statisticians use more accuracy during their RPI calculations, and round only at the end before publishing the results.

The following activity is intended to help you draw together many of the ideas you have met in this section, both about what the RPI is and how it is calculated.

Activity 22   *The effects of particular price changes on the RPI*

Between February 2011 and February 2012, the price of leisure goods fell on average by 2.3%, while the price of canteen meals rose by 2.8%. Answer the following questions about the likely effects of these changes on the value of the RPI. (No calculations are required.)

(a) Looked at in isolation (that is, supposing that no other prices changed), would the change in the price of leisure goods lead to an increase or a decrease in the value of the RPI?

Would the change in the price of canteen meals (looked at in isolation) lead to an increase or a decrease in the value of the RPI?

(b) In each case, is the size of the increase or decrease likely to be large or small?

(c) Using what you know about the structure of the RPI, decide which of 'Leisure goods' and 'Canteen meals' has the larger weight.

(d) Which of the price changes mentioned in the question will have a larger effect on the value of the RPI? Briefly explain your answer.

5.3 Using the price indices

The RPI and CPI are intended to help measure price changes, so we shall start this section by describing how to use them for this purpose.

Example 23   *A news report on inflation*

The BBC News website reported (20 March 2012) 'UK inflation rate falls to 3.4% in February'. What does that actually mean?

The rest of the BBC article makes it clear that this 'inflation' figure was based on the CPI rather than the RPI, but its meaning is still not obvious. What is usually meant in situations like this is the following.

The annual rate of inflation

In the UK, the (annual) rate of inflation is the percentage increase in the value of the CPI (or the RPI) compared to one year earlier.

(In M140, it will always be made clear whether you should use the CPI or the RPI in contexts like this.)

The annual rate of inflation is sometimes called the *year-on-year rate of inflation*.

In February 2012, the CPI was 121.8. Exactly a year earlier, in February 2011, the CPI was 117.8. The ratio of these two values is

$$\frac{\text{value of CPI in February 2012}}{\text{value of CPI in February 2011}} = \frac{121.8}{117.8} \simeq 1.034.$$

So the value of the CPI in February 2012 was 3.4% higher than in the previous February. That is the source of the number in the BBC headline.

Activity 23   *The annual inflation rate in February 2012*

In February 2012, the RPI was 239.9. Exactly a year earlier, in February 2011, the RPI was 231.3. Calculate the annual inflation rate for February 2012, based on the RPI.

The fact that the inflation rates that are generally reported in the media relate to price *increases* (as measured in a price index) over a *whole year* means that one has to be careful in interpreting the figures, in several ways.

- Media reports might say that 'inflation is falling', but this does not mean that *prices* are falling. It simply means that the annual inflation rate is less than it was the previous month. So when the BBC headline said that the (annual) inflation rate had fallen to 3.4% in February 2012, it meant that the February 2012 rate was smaller than the January 2012 rate (which was 3.6%). Prices were still rising, but not quite so quickly.

- The change in price levels over one month may be, and indeed usually is, considerably different from the annual inflation rate. For instance, prices actually fell between December 2011 and January 2012: the CPI was 121.7 in December 2011 and 121.1 in January 2012. (Prices in the UK usually fall between December and January in the UK, as Christmas shopping ends and the January sales begin.) But the annual inflation rate for January 2012, measured by the CPI, was 3.6%.

- The effect of a single major cause of increased prices can persist in the annual inflation rates long after the prices originally increased. For instance, the standard rate of value added tax (VAT) in the UK went up from 17.5% to 20% at the start of January 2011, causing a one-off increase in the price (to consumers) of many goods and services. This showed up in the annual inflation rate for January 2011, where prices were 4.0% higher than a year earlier. Moreover, the annual inflation rate for every other month in 2011 was also affected by the VAT increase, because in each case the CPI was being compared to the CPI in the corresponding month in 2010, before the VAT increase.

Another important use of price indices like the RPI and CPI is for *index-linking*. This is used for such things as savings and pensions, as a means of safeguarding the value of money held or received in these forms.

Index-linking an amount

To index-link any amount of money, the amount in question is multiplied by the same ratio as the change in the value of the price index. Another term for this process is **indexation**.

It is important to stress the notion of *ratio* in index-linking, because it is only by calculating the ratio of two indices that you can get an accurate measure of how prices have increased. For example, an increase in the RPI from 100 to 200 represents a 100% increase in price, whereas a further RPI increase from 200 to 300 represents only a further 50% increase in price.

Example 24   *Index-linking a pension*

The value of the RPI for February 2012 was 239.9 whereas the corresponding figure for February 2011 was 231.3. So an index-linked pension that was, say, £450 per month in February 2011, would be increased to

$$£450 \times \frac{239.9}{231.3} \text{ (i.e. £466.73) per month}$$

for February 2012. The reason for index-linking the pension in this way is that the increased pension would buy the same amount of goods or services in February 2012 as the original pension bought in February 2011 – that is, it should have the same purchasing power.

Pensions can be, and indeed increasingly are, index-linked using the CPI rather than the RPI.

Activity 24   *Index-linking a pension using the CPI*

An index-linked pension was £120 per week in November 2010. It is index-linked using the CPI. How much should the pension be per week in November 2011? The value of the CPI was 115.6 in November 2010 and 121.2 in November 2011.

This principle leads to another much-quoted figure which can be calculated directly from the RPI: **the purchasing power of the pound**. (This is the purchasing power of the pound *within this country*, not its purchasing power abroad; the latter is a distinct and far more complicated concept.) The purchasing power of the pound measures how much a consumer can buy with a fixed amount of money at one point of time compared with another point of time.

The word *compared* here is again important; it makes sense only to talk about the purchasing power of the pound at one time *compared* with another. For example, if £1 worth of goods would have cost only 60p four years ago, then we say that the purchasing power of the pound is only 60p compared with four years earlier.

Purchasing power of the pound

The purchasing power (in pence) of the pound at date A compared with date B is

$$\frac{\text{value of RPI at date B}}{\text{value of RPI at date A}} \times 100.$$

The purchasing power of the pound could be calculated using the CPI instead, though the figures published by the Office for National Statistics do happen to use the RPI.

Example 25 *Calculating the purchasing power of the pound*

(a) The purchasing power of the pound in February 2012 compared with February 2011 was

231.3 and 239.9 are the two RPI values given in Activity 23.

$$\frac{231.3}{239.9} \times 100\text{p} = 96.415\,17\text{p}.$$

We round this to give 96p.

(b) The purchasing power of the pound in February 2012 compared with the base date, January 1987, was

$$\frac{100}{239.9} \times 100\text{p}.$$

(At the base date, the value of the RPI is 100 by definition.)

This is, after rounding, 42p.

Activity 25 *Annual inflation and the purchasing power of the pound*

Table 15 Values of the RPI from January 2009 to December 2011

Month	2009	2010	2011	Month	2009	2010	2011
January	210.1	217.9	229.0	July	213.4	223.6	234.7
February	211.4	219.2	231.3	August	214.4	224.5	236.1
March	211.3	220.7	232.5	September	215.3	225.3	237.9
April	211.5	222.8	234.4	October	216.0	225.8	238.0
May	212.8	223.6	235.2	November	216.6	226.8	238.5
June	213.4	224.1	235.2	December	218.0	228.4	239.4

(Source: Office for National Statistics)

For each of the following months, use the values of the RPI in Table 15 to calculate the annual inflation rate (based on the RPI) and to calculate the purchasing power of the pound (in pence) compared to one year previously.

(a) May 2010   (b) October 2011   (c) March 2011

You have seen that the RPI can be used as a way of updating the value of a pension to take account of general increases in prices (index-linking). The RPI is used in other similar ways, for instance to update the levels of some other state benefits and investments. But the CPI *could* be used for these purposes.

Why are there two different indices? Let's look at how this arose. As well as its use for index-linking, which is basically to compensate for price changes, the RPI previously played an important role in the management of the UK economy generally. The government sets targets for the rate of inflation, and the Bank of England Monetary Policy Committee adjusts interest rates to try to achieve these targets. Until the end of 2003, these inflation targets were based on the RPI, or to be precise, on another price index called RPIX which is similar to the RPI but omits owner-occupiers' mortgage interest payments from the calculations. (There are good economic reasons for this omission, to do with the fact that in many ways the purchase of a house has the character of a long-term investment, unlike the purchase of, say, a bag of potatoes.) From 2004, the inflation targets have instead been set in terms of the CPI. The CPI is calculated in a way that matches similar inflation measures in other countries of the European Union. (So it can be used for international comparisons.)

In terms of general principles, though, and also in terms of most of the details of how the indices are calculated, the differences between the RPI and CPI are not actually very great. As mentioned in Subsection 5.1, the CPI reflects the spending of a wider population than the RPI. Partly because of this, there are certain items (e.g. university accommodation fees) that are included in the CPI but not the RPI. There are also certain items that are included in the RPI but not the CPI, notably some owner-occupiers' housing costs such as mortgage interest payments and house-building insurance. Finally, the CPI uses a different method to the RPI for combining individual price measurements.

Because of these differences, inflation as measured by the CPI tends usually to be rather lower than that measured by the RPI. In Example 23, you saw that the annual inflation rate in February 2012 as measured by the CPI was 3.4%. The annual inflation rate in the same month, as measured by the RPI, was 3.7%, as you saw in Activity 23. The RPI continues to be calculated and published, and to be used to index-link payments such as savings rates and some pensions. However, there are reasons why the RPI is more appropriate than the CPI for *some* such purposes, and it seems likely to continue in use for a long time. Furthermore, changes in how index-linking is done can be politically very controversial. For instance, in 2010, the UK government announced that in future, public sector pensions would be index-linked to the CPI rather than the RPI, which caused major complaints from those affected (because inflation as measured by the CPI is usually lower than that measured using the RPI, so pensions will not increase so much in money terms).

Arguably it is rather strange to use the RPI to index pensions, given that (as was said at the beginning of Subsection 5.1) the RPI omits the expenditure of pensioner households.

You might be asking yourself which is the 'correct' measure of inflation – RPI, CPI, or something else entirely. There is no such thing as a single 'correct' measure. Different measures are appropriate for different purposes. That's why it is important to understand just what is being measured and how.

In this section, you have seen how price rises are measured using an index of retail prices. Earnings are discussed in the next unit. Only when prices and earnings have both been considered can you begin to answer the central question of these two units: *Are people getting better or worse off?* In the next unit, you will see how to use a price index in conjunction with an index of earnings to see whether rises in earnings are keeping pace with rises in prices.

Exercises on Section 5

Exercise 10   *Calculating the RPI for February 2012*

Find the value of the RPI in February 2012, using the data in the table below. The value of the RPI in January 2012 was 238.0.

Table 16   Calculating the RPI for February 2012

Group	Price ratio for February 2012 relative to January 2012 r	2012 weights w	Price ratio × weight rw
Food and catering	1.009	161	
Alcohol and tobacco	1.005	85	
Housing and household expenditure	1.003	412	
Personal expenditure	1.040	84	
Travel and leisure	1.005	258	
Total			

(Source: Office for National Statistics)

Exercise 11   *Annual inflation rates and the purchasing power of the pound*

For each of the following months, use Table 15 (in Subsection 5.3) to calculate the annual inflation rate given by the RPI and to calculate the purchasing power of the pound (in pence) compared to one year previously.

(a) October 2010

(b) January 2011

Exercise 12   *Index-linking another pension*

An index-linked pension (linked to the RPI) was £800 per month in April 2010. How much should it be in April 2011? (Again, use the RPI values in Table 15.)

6 Computer work: measures of location

In Subsection 1.4, you learned that the median is a resistant measure and the mean is a sensitive measure. You will explore what this means in practice for a particular dataset and then verify the rules for weighted means for a particular example. You should work through all of Chapter 2 of the Computer Book now, if you have not already done so.

Summary

In this unit you have been discovering how statistics can be used to answer questions about prices. You have learned how to find a single number to summarise the price of an item at a particular point in time, even though the item might be available from a number of sources. You have also learned how to combine information on prices across a range of goods and services. Then, through the use of price ratios, you have seen how changes in price over time can be quantified. In particular, you have learned about chained price indices such as the Retail Prices Index (RPI) and Consumer Prices Index (CPI), used in the UK to measure inflation.

Two more measures of location, the mean and weighted mean, have been introduced. The mean is a *sensitive* measure whereas the median is a *resistant* measure. The weighted mean only depends on the relative sizes of the weights, and the weighted mean of two numbers is always closer to the value with the highest weight.

You have learned about measures of spread, in particular the range and the interquartile range, and about quartiles, from which the interquartile range is calculated. The five-figure summary was described, which consists of the minimum, lower quartile, median, upper quartile and maximum, along with the size of the batch. A way of displaying the five-figure summary, the boxplot, was introduced. The 'box' in the boxplot runs between the lower and upper quartiles and has a line in it corresponding to the median, thus displaying three of the five numbers in the five-number summary. The other two numbers in the five-number summary, the minimum and maximum, are given by the lengths of the whiskers or position of potential outliers.

You have learned how the RPI and the CPI are calculated by the Office for National Statistics from a 'basket' of goods using weighted means to give price ratios, group price ratios and all-commodities price ratios. These all-commodity price ratios are then chained to give the value of the index relative to a base date. The RPI and CPI can be used to calculate inflation, to index-link amounts of money and to calculate the purchasing power of the pound at one time compared with another.

Learning outcomes

After working through this unit, you should be able to:

- find the median of a batch of data
- find the mean of a batch of data
- describe what is meant by a resistant measure of location, and identify which measures are resistant
- find the weighted mean of two numbers with associated weights
- use the weighted mean to combine two batch means to find the mean of the combined batch
- use the weighted mean to find the overall average cost of a commodity from the price paid and quantity purchased on two occasions
- understand the use of a weighted mean in other contexts and for larger sets of numbers
- find the upper and lower quartiles and the interquartile range of a batch of data
- prepare a five-figure summary of a batch of data
- interpret the boxplot of a batch of data
- use the boxplot to investigate the overall shape of a batch of data, in particular its symmetry and skewness
- calculate a simple chained price index and explain what is meant by its base date
- describe the major steps in producing the Retail Prices Index
- calculate the value of the Retail Prices Index from the five group price ratios and weights
- use the Retail Prices Index or the Consumer Prices Index to compare the general level of prices at two dates and calculate the rise in the general level of prices over a year (the annual rate of inflation)
- use the Retail Prices Index or the Consumer Prices Index to do index-linking calculations, and use the Retail Prices Index to find the purchasing power of the pound at one date compared with another.

Solutions to activities

Solution to Activity 1

For a batch size of 20, the median position is $\frac{1}{2}(20+1) = 10\frac{1}{2}$. So, the median will be halfway between $x_{(10)}$ and $x_{(11)}$. These are both 150, so the median is £150.

Solution to Activity 2

(a) A stemplot of all 14 prices in the table is shown below.

```
374 │ 0 0 3
375 │
376 │ 0 7
377 │ 6
378 │ 4
379 │ 5 6
380 │ 1 1 4 5
381 │ 8
```

$n = 14$ 374 │ 0 represents 3.740p per kWh

Stemplot of 14 gas prices

(b) Stemplots for the prices for northern and southern cities are shown below.

Northern

```
374 │ 0 0
375 │
376 │ 7
377 │ 6
378 │
379 │
380 │ 1 1 4
```

Southern

```
374 │ 3
375 │
376 │ 0
377 │
378 │ 4
379 │ 5 6
380 │ 5
381 │ 8
```

$n = 7$ 374 │ 0 represents 3.740p per kWh

$n = 7$ 374 │ 3 represents 3.743p per kWh

Stemplots for northern and southern cities separately.

(c) For a batch size of 14, the median position is $\frac{1}{2}(14+1) = 7\frac{1}{2}$. So, the all-cities median will be halfway between $x_{(7)}$ and $x_{(8)}$. These are 3.784 and 3.795, so the median is 3.7895, which is 3.790 when rounded to three decimal places. (The rounded median should be written as 3.790 and not 3.79, to show it is accurate to three decimal places and not just two.)

For the northern and southern batches, both of size 7, the median for each is the value of $x_{(4)}$ (that is, $\frac{1}{2}(7+1) = 4$). This is 3.776 for the northern batch and 3.795 for the southern batch.

The range is the difference between the upper extreme, E_U, and the lower extreme, E_L (range $= E_U - E_L$). So the all-cities range is

$$3.818 - 3.740 = 0.078,$$

the range for the northern batch is

$$3.804 - 3.740 = 0.064,$$

and the range for the southern batch is

$$3.818 - 3.743 = 0.075.$$

The medians and ranges are summarised below.

	Median	Range
All cities	3.790	0.078
Northern cities	3.776	0.064
Southern cities	3.795	0.075

Thus the general level of gas prices in the country as a whole was about 3.790p per kWh. The average price differed by only 0.078p per kWh across the 14 cities.

The difference between the median prices for the northern and southern cities is 0.019p per kWh ($3.795 - 3.776 = 0.019$), with the south having the higher median.

The analysis does not clearly reveal whether the general level of gas prices for typical consumers in 2010 was higher in the south or in the north, though there is an indication that prices were a little higher in the south. The range of prices was also rather greater in the south. It is worth noting that the differences in gas prices between the cities in Table 3 were generally small, when measured in pence per kWh – although, with a typical annual gas usage of 18 000 kWh, the price difference between the most expensive city and the cheapest would amount to an annual difference in bills of about £14 on a typical bill of somewhere around £700.

Solution to Activity 3

Using the data for the prices from Activity 1:

$$\text{mean} = \frac{\text{sum}}{\text{size}} = \frac{90 + 100 + \ldots + 270}{20} = £162.$$

Or using the $\sum$ notation, $\sum x = 90 + 100 + \ldots + 270 = 3240$ and $n = 20$, so

$$\text{mean} = \bar{x} = \frac{\sum x}{n} = \frac{3240}{20} = £162.$$

The prices were rounded to the nearest £10, so it is appropriate to keep one more significant figure for the mean, that is, to show it accurate to the nearest £1. So since the exact value is £162, it needs no further rounding.

Solution to Activity 4

	Mean	Median
The entries are	3.7859	3.795
	3.7996	3.796

Whereas deletion of Cardiff and Ipswich has the effect of increasing the mean price by 0.0137p per kWh, the median price increases by only 0.001p per kWh. This is what we would expect as, in general, the more resistant a measure is, the less it changes when a few extreme values are deleted.

Solution to Activity 5

	Mean	Median
The entries are	3.7996	3.796
	4.6996	3.796

Here the median is completely unaffected by the misprint, although the mean changes considerably.

Solution to Activity 6

You should expect the weighted mean price to be nearer the London price, because of Rule 2 for weighted means (Subsection 2.1) and given that London has a much larger weight then Edinburgh.

The weighted mean price given by the formula in Example 11 is (after rounding) 3.814p per kWh, which is indeed much closer to the London price than to the Edinburgh price.

Solution to Activity 7

(a) $\text{OCAS} = \dfrac{(80 \times 50) + (60 \times 50)}{50 + 50} = \dfrac{4000 + 3000}{100} = \dfrac{7000}{100} = 70.$

This is the same as a simple (unweighted) mean of the two scores, because the two component scores have equal weight. It lies exactly halfway between the two scores ($\frac{1}{2}(80 + 60) = 70$).

(b) $\text{OCAS} = \dfrac{(80 \times 40) + (60 \times 60)}{40 + 60} = \dfrac{3200 + 3600}{100} = \dfrac{6800}{100} = 68.$

This is slightly less than the simple mean in (a) because the component with the lower score (TMA) has the greater weight.

(c) $\text{OCAS} = \dfrac{(80 \times 65) + (60 \times 55)}{65 + 55} = \dfrac{5200 + 3300}{120} = \dfrac{8500}{120} \simeq 70.8.$

This is slightly higher than the simple mean in (a) because the component with the higher score (iCMA) has the greater weight.

(Note that the weights need not necessarily sum to 100, even when dealing with percentages.)

(d) $\text{OCAS} = \dfrac{(80 \times 25) + (60 \times 75)}{25 + 75} = \dfrac{2000 + 4500}{100} = \dfrac{6500}{100} = 65.$

This is even lower than (b), so even nearer the lower score (TMA), because the TMA score has even greater weight.

(e) $\text{OCAS} = \dfrac{(80 \times 30) + (60 \times 90)}{30 + 90} = \dfrac{2400 + 5400}{120} = \dfrac{7800}{120} = 65.$

This is the same as (d) because the ratios of the weights are the same; they are both in the ratio 1 to 3. That is, $25 : 75 = 30 : 90 \ (= 1 : 3)$.

(We say this as follows: 'the ratio 25 to 75 equals the ratio 30 to 90'.)

Solution to Activity 9

The table showing the required sums (and the values in the xw column, that you may not have had to write down), is as follows.

	Price (p/kWh) x	Weight w	Price × weight xw
Aberdeen	13.76	19	261.44
Belfast	15.03	58	871.74
Edinburgh	13.86	42	582.12
Leeds	12.70	150	1 905.00
Liverpool	13.89	82	1 138.98
Manchester	12.65	224	2 833.60
Newcastle-upon-Tyne	12.97	88	1 141.36
Nottingham	12.64	67	846.88
Birmingham	12.89	228	2 938.92
Canterbury	12.92	5	64.60
Cardiff	13.83	33	456.39
Ipswich	12.84	14	179.76
London	13.17	828	10 904.76
Plymouth	13.61	24	326.64
Southampton	13.41	30	402.30
Sum		1892	24 854.49

Thus $\sum xw = 24\,854.49$, $\sum w = 1892$ and

$$\frac{\sum xw}{\sum w} = \frac{24\,854.49}{1892} = 13.136\,623 \simeq 13.14.$$

So the weighted mean of electricity prices is 13.14p per kWh.

Solution to Activity 10

(a) Here, because $n = 15$, an appropriate picture of the data would be Figure 9. To find the lower and upper quartiles, Q_1 and Q_3, of this batch, first find $\frac{1}{4}(n + 1) = 4$ and $\frac{3}{4}(n + 1) = 12$. Therefore $Q_1 = 268\text{p}$ and $Q_3 = 299\text{p}$.

(b) For this batch, $n = 14$ so $\frac{1}{4}(n + 1) = 3\frac{3}{4}$ and $\frac{3}{4}(n + 1) = 11\frac{1}{4}$.

$$Q_1 = 3.743 + \tfrac{3}{4}(3.760 - 3.743)$$
$$= 3.755\,75 \simeq 3.756$$

and

$$Q_3 = 3.801 + \tfrac{1}{4}(3.804 - 3.801)$$
$$= 3.801\,75 \simeq 3.802.$$

So the lower quartile is 3.756 p per kWh and the upper quartile is 3.802p per kWh.

Solution to Activity 11

The range is the distance between the extremes:

$$\text{range} = E_U - E_L$$
$$= 369\text{p} - 268\text{p}$$
$$= 101\text{p}.$$

The interquartile range is the distance between the quartiles:

$$\text{IQR} = Q_3 - Q_1$$
$$= 299\text{p} - 268\text{p}$$
$$= 31\text{p}.$$

Solution to Activity 12

The quartiles, before rounding, are $Q_1 = 3.755\,75$ and $Q_3 = 3.801\,75$. So

$$\text{IQR} = Q_3 - Q_1$$
$$= 3.801\,75 - 3.755\,75$$
$$= 0.046,$$

and the interquartile range is 0.046p per kWh.

Solution to Activity 13

(a) All the necessary figures have already been calculated. You found the median (3.790) in Activity 2 and the quartiles ($Q_1 = 3.756$, $Q_3 = 3.802$) in Activity 10. The extremes ($E_L = 3.740$, $E_U = 3.818$) and the batch size ($n = 14$) are clearly shown in the stemplot.

So the five-figure summary is as follows:

		3.790	
$n = 14$	3.756		3.802
	3.740		3.818

(b) Looking at the stemplot, on the whole the lower values are more spread out, indicating that the data are not symmetric and are left-skew.

The central box of the boxplot again shows left skewness, with the left-hand part of the box being clearly longer than the right-hand part. However, this skewness does not show up in the lengths of the whiskers in this batch – they are both the same length.

Solution to Activity 14

The increase (in £/MWh) is $29 - 24 = 5$. This is $\frac{5}{24} \simeq 0.208$ as a proportion of the 2007 price. That is, $\frac{5}{24} \times 100\% \simeq 20.8\%$ of the 2007 price. Or you might have worked this out by finding that the 2008 price is $\frac{29}{24} \times 100\% \simeq 120.8\%$ of the 2007 price, so that again the increase is 20.8% of the 2007 price.

Solution to Activity 15

The 2008 electricity price is $1.145 \times 100\% = 114.5\%$ of the 2007 price, so that the increase is 14.5% of the 2007 price.

The 2008 value of the electricity price index is

(value of the index in 2007, which is 100)

$\times$ (electricity price ratio for 2008 relative to 2007)

$= 100 \times 1.145 = 114.5.$

Solution to Activity 16

The expenditure on a particular fuel in a particular year can be calculated as expenditure = quantity used $\times$ price. Therefore, if the expenditure and price are known, the quantity used can be calculated as

$$\text{quantity used} = \frac{\text{expenditure}}{\text{price}}.$$

In 2007, Gradgrind's gas cost £24 per MWh, and they spent £9298 on gas, so the amount of gas they used in MWh was

$$\frac{9298}{24} \simeq 387.4.$$

The other amounts, in MWh, are found in a similar way, and all are shown in the following table.

	2007	2008
Gas	387.4	280.9
Electricity	42.2	34.4

The reason that the expenditures went down is simply that Gradgrind used less of each fuel in 2008 than in 2007.

Solution to Activity 17

(a) The gas price ratio for 2009 relative to 2008 is

$$\frac{30}{29} \simeq 1.034.$$

The electricity price ratio for 2009 relative to 2008 is

$$\frac{98}{87} \simeq 1.126.$$

(Over this year, electricity prices rose a lot more than gas prices.)

(b) The overall energy price ratio for 2009 relative to 2008 is

$$\frac{(1.034 \times 8145) + (1.126 \times 2991)}{8145 + 2991} = \frac{11\,789.796}{11\,136} \simeq 1.059.$$

(c) Using the 2009 expenditures for weights instead of the 2008 expenditures, the overall energy price ratio for 2009 relative to 2008 is

$$\frac{(1.034 \times 23\,733) + (1.126 \times 2275)}{23\,733 + 2275} = \frac{27\,101.572}{26\,008} \simeq 1.042.$$

This price ratio is considerably less than the one found in part (b).

(Note that if full calculator accuracy is retained throughout the calculations, the price ratio is 1.043 to three decimal places.)

Solution to Activity 18

The gas price ratio for 2010 relative to 2009 is

$$\frac{28}{30} \simeq 0.933.$$

The electricity price ratio for 2010 relative to 2009 is

$$\frac{88}{98} \simeq 0.898.$$

(Both price ratios are less than 1 because, over this year, Gradgrind's gas and electricity prices both fell.)

The overall energy price ratio for 2010 relative to 2009 is

$$\frac{(0.933 \times 23\,733) + (0.898 \times 2275)}{23\,733 + 2275} = \frac{24\,185.839}{26\,008} \simeq 0.930.$$

Then the value of the index for 2010 is found by multiplying the 2009 value of the index by this overall price ratio, giving

$$126.2 \times 0.930 \simeq 117.4.$$

Solution to Activity 19

(a) What you need to remember here is that the size of an area represents the proportion of expenditure on that class of goods or services. (Also, it is admittedly not very easy to estimate these areas 'by eye'! Your estimates might quite reasonably differ from those given here.)

- The sector for 'Personal expenditure' looks as if it is approximately a tenth of the whole inner circle – so approximately a tenth of total expenditure is personal expenditure.

- 'Housing and household expenditure' looks as if it is somewhere between a third and a half of the inner circle – perhaps approximately two fifths – so approximately two fifths of expenditure is on housing and household expenditure.

- The area for 'Housing' takes up about a quarter of the outer ring, so about a quarter of expenditure is on housing.

(b) The amount spent each week on 'Personal expenditure' is approximately

$$\frac{1}{10} \times £540 = £54.$$

The amount spent each week on 'Housing and household expenditure' is approximately

$$\frac{2}{5} \times £540 = £216 \simeq £220.$$

The amount spent each week on 'Housing' is approximately

$$\frac{1}{4} \times £540 = £135 \simeq £140.$$

Recall, however, that the weights represent *average* proportions of expenditure, and the spending patterns of the selected household may differ from those of the 'typical' household.

Solution to Activity 20

Every household will be different, but think about the reasons for any large differences between your weights and those for the RPI.

Solution to Activity 21

Group	Price ratio for July 2011 relative to January 2011 r	2011 weights w	Price ratio × weight rw
Food and catering	1.024	165	168.960
Alcohol and tobacco	1.042	88	91.696
Housing and household expenditure	1.012	408	412.896
Personal expenditure	1.053	82	86.346
Travel and leisure	1.030	257	264.710
Sum		1000	1024.608

$$\text{sum } (w) = 1000, \quad \text{sum of products } (rw) = 1024.608,$$

$$\text{all-item price ratio} = \frac{\text{sum of products } (rw)}{\text{sum}(w)} = \frac{1024.608}{1000}$$
$$= 1.024\,608,$$

$$\text{value of RPI in July 2011} = 229.0 \times 1.024\,608$$
$$= 234.635\,232$$
$$\simeq 234.6.$$

Solution to Activity 22

More detail has been included in these comments than is expected from you. When you read them, make sure you understand all the points mentioned.

(a) The RPI is calculated using the price ratio and weight of each item. Since the weights of items change very little from one year to the next, the price ratio alone will normally tell you whether a change in price is likely to lead to an increase or a decrease in the value of the RPI. If a price rises, then the price ratio is greater than one, so the RPI is likely to increase as a result. If a price falls, then the price ratio is less than one, so the RPI is likely to decrease. Therefore, since the price of leisure goods fell, this is likely to lead to a decrease in the value of the RPI. For a similar reason, the increase in the price of canteen meals is likely to lead to an increase in the value of the RPI.

(b) Both changes are likely to be small for two reasons. First, the price changes are themselves fairly small. Second, leisure goods and canteen meals form only part of a household's expenditure: no single group, subgroup or section will have a large effect on the RPI on its own, unless there is a very large change in its price.

(c) The weight of 'Leisure goods' was 33 in 2012 (see Table 12). Since 'Canteen meals' is only one section in the subgroup 'Catering', which had weight 47 in 2012, the weight of 'Canteen meals' will be much smaller than 47. (In fact it was 3.) So the weight of 'Leisure goods' is much larger than the weight of 'Canteen meals'.

(d) Since the weight of 'Leisure goods' is much larger than the weight of 'Canteen meals', and the percentage change in the prices are not too different in size, the change in the price of leisure goods is likely to have a much larger effect on the value of the RPI as a whole.

Solution to Activity 23

The ratio of the two RPI values is
$$\frac{\text{value of RPI in February 2012}}{\text{value of RPI in February 2011}} = \frac{239.9}{231.3} \simeq 1.037,$$
or 103.7%. Therefore the annual inflation rate, based on the RPI was 3.7%. (Note that this is slightly higher than the annual inflation rate measured using the CPI.)

Solution to Activity 24

The weekly amount in November 2011 should be

$$£120 \times \frac{121.2}{115.6} \simeq £125.81.$$

Solution to Activity 25

(a) For May 2010, the ratio of the value of the RPI to its value one year earlier is

$$\frac{223.6}{212.8} \simeq 1.051,$$

so the annual inflation rate is 5.1%.

The purchasing power of the pound compared to one year previously is

$$\frac{212.8}{223.6} \times 100p \simeq 95p.$$

(b) For October 2011, the ratio of the value of the RPI to its value one year earlier is

$$\frac{238.0}{225.8} \simeq 1.054,$$

so the annual inflation rate is 5.4%.

The purchasing power of the pound compared to one year previously is

$$\frac{225.8}{238.0} \times 100p \simeq 95p.$$

(c) For March 2011, the ratio of the value of the RPI to its value one year earlier is

$$\frac{232.5}{220.7} \simeq 1.053,$$

so the annual inflation rate is 5.3%.

The purchasing power of the pound compared to one year previously is

$$\frac{220.7}{232.5} \times 100p \simeq 95p.$$

Solutions to exercises

Solution to Exercise 1

(a) For the arithmetic scores, the position of the median is $\frac{1}{2}(33+1) = 17$, so the median is 79%.

(b) For the television prices, the position of the median is $\frac{1}{2}(26+1) = 13\frac{1}{2}$, so the median is halfway between $x_{(13)}$ and $x_{(14)}$. Thus, the median is

$$\tfrac{1}{2}(\pounds269 + \pounds270) = \pounds269.5 \simeq \pounds270.$$

Solution to Exercise 2

For the batch of arithmetic scores in part (a) of Exercise 1, the sum of the 33 values is 2326 and

$$\frac{2326}{33} \simeq 70.5.$$

Therefore, the mean is 70.5%. (The original data are given to the nearest whole number, so the mean is rounded to one decimal place.)

For the batch of television prices in part (b) of Exercise 1, the sum of the 26 values is 7856 and

$$\frac{7856}{26} = 302.1538 \simeq 302.2.$$

Therefore, the mean is £302.2.

Solution to Exercise 3

For the median, there are now 17 prices left in the batch, so the median is at position $\frac{1}{2}(17+1) = 9$. It is therefore 150.

The sum of the remaining 17 values is 2480, so the mean is

$$\frac{2480}{17} = 145.8824 \simeq 146.$$

In this case, removing the three highest prices has not changed the median at all, but it has reduced the mean considerably. This illustrates that the median is a more resistant measure than the mean.

Solution to Exercise 4

Mean price of all the cameras is

$$\frac{(80.7 \times 10) + (78.5 \times 17)}{10 + 17} = \frac{2141.5}{27},$$

which is £79.3 (rounded to the same accuracy as the original means).

Solution to Exercise 5

Mean price of all the material is

$$\frac{(10.95 \times 8.5) + (12.70 \times 6)}{8.5 + 6} = \frac{169.275}{14.5},$$

which is £11.67 (rounded to the nearest penny).

Solution to Exercise 6

(a) For the arithmetic scores, $n = 33$ so $\frac{1}{4}(n+1) = 8\frac{1}{2}$ and $\frac{3}{4}(n+1) = 25\frac{1}{2}$.

The lower quartile is therefore

$$Q_1 = \frac{1}{2}(55 + 58)\% = 56.5\% \simeq 57\%.$$

The upper quartile is

$$Q_3 = \frac{1}{2}(86 + 89)\% = 87.5\% \simeq 88\%.$$

The interquartile range is

$$Q_3 - Q_1 = 87.5\% - 56.5\% = 31\%.$$

(b) For the television prices, $n = 26$ so $\frac{1}{4}(n+1) = 6\frac{3}{4}$ and $\frac{3}{4}(n+1) = 20\frac{1}{4}$.

The lower quartile is therefore

$$Q_1 = \pounds229 + \frac{3}{4}(\pounds230 - \pounds229) = \pounds229.75 \simeq \pounds230.$$

The upper quartile is

$$Q_3 = \pounds320 + \frac{1}{4}(\pounds349 - \pounds320) = \pounds327.25 \simeq \pounds327.$$

The interquartile range is

$$Q_3 - Q_1 = \pounds327.25 - \pounds229.75 = \pounds97.5 \simeq \pounds98.$$

Solution to Exercise 7

(a) Arithmetic scores:

From the stemplot, $n = 33$, $E_L = 7$ and $E_U = 100$.

	79	
$n = 33$ 57		88
7		100

Five-figure summary of arithmetic scores

(b) Television prices:

From the data table, $n = 26$, $E_L = 170$ and $E_U = 699$.

	270	
$n = 26$ 230		327
170		699

Five-figure summary of television prices

Solution to Exercise 8

For the boxplot of arithmetic scores, the left part of the box is longer than the right part, and the left whisker is also considerably longer than the right. This batch is left-skew (as was also found in Unit 1 (Activity 20, Subsection 5.2)).

For the boxplot of television prices, the right part of the box is rather longer than the left part. The right whisker is also rather longer than the left, and if one also takes into account the fact that two potential outliers have been marked, the top 25% of the data are clearly much more spread out than the bottom 25%. This batch is right-skew.

Solution to Exercise 9

The gas price ratio for 2011 relative to 2010 is

$$\frac{30}{28} \simeq 1.071.$$

The electricity price ratio for 2011 relative to 2010 is

$$\frac{86}{88} \simeq 0.977.$$

The overall energy price ratio for 2011 relative to 2010 is

$$\frac{(1.071 \times 23\,969) + (0.977 \times 2920)}{23\,969 + 2920} = \frac{28\,523.639}{26\,889} \simeq 1.061.$$

Then the value of the index for 2011 is found by multiplying the 2010 value of the index by this overall price ratio, giving

$$117.4 \times 1.061 \simeq 124.6.$$

Solution to Exercise 10

$$\sum w = 1000, \quad \sum rw = 1007.760,$$

$$\text{all-item price ratio} = \frac{\sum rw}{\sum w} = \frac{1007.760}{1000}$$
$$= 1.007\,760,$$

$$\text{value of RPI in February } 2012 = 238.0 \times 1.007\,760$$
$$= 239.846\,88$$
$$\simeq 239.8.$$

(The published index was 239.9. Again, the difference between this and your calculated value is because the ONS statisticians used more accuracy in their intermediate calculations.)

Solution to Exercise 11

(a) For October 2010, the ratio of the value of the RPI to its value one year earlier is

$$\frac{225.8}{216.0} \simeq 1.045,$$

so the annual inflation rate is 4.5%.

The purchasing power of the pound compared to one year previously is

$$\frac{216.0}{225.8} \times 100\text{p} \simeq 96\text{p}.$$

(b) For January 2011, the ratio of the value of the RPI to its value one year earlier is

$$\frac{229.0}{217.9} \simeq 1.051,$$

so the annual inflation rate is 5.1%.

The purchasing power of the pound compared to one year previously is

$$\frac{217.9}{229.0} \times 100\text{p} \simeq 95\text{p}.$$

Solution to Exercise 12

The RPI for April 2011 was 234.4 and the RPI for April 2010 was 222.8. So in April 2011, the pension should be

$$£800 \times \frac{234.4}{222.8} \simeq £842 \text{ per month.}$$

Acknowledgements

Grateful acknowledgement is made to the following sources:

Table 3 Adapted from: https://www.gov.uk/government/statistical-data-sets/annual-domestic-energy-price-statistics

Table 5 Taken from:
http://en.wikipedia.org/wiki/List_of_conurbations_in_the_United_Kingdom.
This file is licensed under the Creative Commons Attribution Licence
http://creativecommons.org/licenses/by/3.0/

Table 6 Department of Energy and Climate Change

Tables 13–15 Office for National Statistics licensed under the
Open Government Licence v.1.0

Table 16 Adapted from data from the Office for National Statistics licensed
under the Open Government Licence v.1.0

Figure 28 Crown copyright material is reproduced under Class Licence
Number C01W0000065 with the permission of the Controller, Office of
Public Sector Information (OPSI)

Subsection 1.1 figure, 'Data, data, data!', Mary Evans Picture Library

Subsection 1.2 figure, 'An upside down V-shape', GIDZY /
www.flickr.com. This file is licensed under the Creative Commons
Attribution Licence http://creativecommons.org/licenses/by/3.0/

Subsection 1.2 figure, 'Not that kind of flat screen', Joey Gannon /
www.flickr.com. This file is licensed under the Creative Commons
Attribution-Share Alike Licence
http://creativecommons.org/licenses/by-sa/3.0/

Subsection 3.2 figure, 'More birds, now showing the shape of the ∧∧
diagram', JUMBERO / www.flickr.com. This file is licensed under the
Creative Commons Attribution-Share Alike Licence
http://creativecommons.org/licenses/by-sa/3.0/

Subsection 3.3 quote from McCullagh, P. (2003): The Royal Statistical
Society

Subsection 3.3 photo of John Tukey: Taken from
http://rchsbowman.wordpress.com/2011/09/03/statistics-notes-
%E2%80%94-biography-%E2%80%94-john-wilder-tukey/

Subsection 3.3 cartoon: www.causeweb.org

Subsection 5.2 quote from BBC News website, 14 March 2012: Taken from
www.bbc.co.uk/news/business-17356286

Every effort has been made to contact copyright holders. If any have been
inadvertently overlooked the publishers will be pleased to make the
necessary arrangements at the first opportunity.

Unit 3

Earnings

Introduction

It is a commonplace observation that men earn more than women. (This is often described as a 'gender differential' in pay.) But how much more? And why? These are questions we shall look at in the first section of this unit. Statistics, by its nature, is far better at answering *how much?* questions than at answering *why?* questions, so we shall concentrate on the former.

In Section 1, we consider the problem of how to compare the earnings of men and women. There are two parts to this problem.

- Finding data which adequately summarise the earnings of all the men and women in the country.

- Finding a measure of the difference between men's and women's earnings based on the available data.

Whilst continuing to look at data on earnings, Sections 2 and 3 revise the techniques for presenting and summarising data which you have used in the first two units of the module, and introduce some new ones. In particular, Section 3 introduces another widely used measure of spread: the standard deviation.

In Section 4, you will use Minitab to do further numerical calculations on data and to draw boxplots.

The final section ties together the central themes of Units 2 and 3 by comparing two important measures – the Consumer Prices Index (CPI) and the Average Weekly Earnings (AWE) index. Taken together, these two indices may help us answer the central question of this unit and the previous one: *Are people getting better or worse off?*

In planning your study, you should note that Section 1 is considerably longer than the other sections in the unit.

Also note that you will be guided to the Computer Book at the end of Subsection 3.1 and in Section 4. Like Unit 2, it is better to do the work at those points in the text, although you can leave it until later if you prefer.

1 Gender and earnings

In this section, the plan is to investigate the relationship between gender and earnings. How should we start this investigation?

In Unit 1 you were introduced to an approach to statistical investigations which is summarised in the four stages of Figure 1.

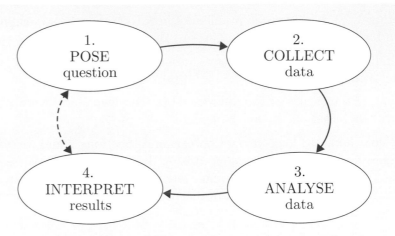

Figure 1   The modelling diagram

So let us follow this plan and start by posing a precise question.

(Throughout Section 1, numbered boxes corresponding to this diagram will be used to point out which of the four stages we are at.)

1.1   Posing the question

Earnings are affected by a great variety of factors apart from gender, including the hours worked, as well as a person's background, training, aptitude and ability. It is useful to illustrate the relationship between earnings and these factors using a diagram like Figure 2.

1. Pose

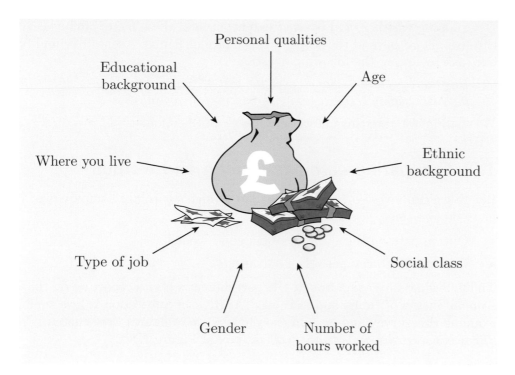

Figure 2   Some of the factors influencing earnings

Note that gender is one of the factors included in Figure 2, but several other factors are included too. Some of these may be more important than gender in determining levels of earnings. One problem in analysing these factors is that they are all interrelated with gender. For example:

- Women may have a different educational background from men, so it is difficult to say whether the differences between men's and women's earnings are really due to gender or whether they are due to educational background.

- More women than men are part-time workers, so the differences in their earnings may be due to this.

- Some jobs are done predominantly by women, others mainly by men, and earnings vary historically from job to job, so this is another possible reason for differences in earnings.

In social research, problems such as this are common, and it is usually impossible to disentangle completely the effects of the various factors. However, we can go some way towards disentanglement: instead of looking at *all* men and *all* women, we shall concentrate on men and women who are similar with respect to the other variables, so that we compare like with like.

This may not be a straightforward process. A researcher will often know what comparisons he or she would like to make, but available data may not provide the necessary information. There are also the practical constraints of limited time, money, energy and patience to carry out such an investigation. Therefore, *comparing like with like* depends on what is possible and practical.

Determining whether, and to what extent, each of these factors influences earnings, is far beyond the scope of this module. It makes sense to simplify our task by asking the following question.

Has there been any change over the last 15 years or so (up to 2012) in the discrepancy between women's and men's earnings?

We shall investigate this question in the rest of Section 1.

1.2 Comparing earnings of men and women

Before we can investigate how men's and women's earnings compare, we must do two things:

- Obtain data on the earnings of men and women.

- Decide how to compare their earnings.

The following data come from a UK government website reporting on the Annual Survey of Hours and Earnings (ASHE); in Subsection 1.3 we shall examine this survey and explain exactly why these figures were chosen. (That stage corresponds to the 'collect' box in Figure 1.)

> ### The Equal Pay Act 1970
>
> In 1968, at the Ford car factory in Dagenham, there were 850 women machinists who went on strike for equal pay because they were paid 15% less than men for doing the same work. In the aftermath of their action, the UK parliament passed the Equal Pay Act 1970 that prohibited less favourable treatment between men and women in their terms of employment.
>
> The Act gave an individual a right to the same contractual pay and benefits as a person of the opposite sex in the same employment, where the man and the woman were doing:
>
> - like work; or
>
> - work rated as equivalent under an analytical job evaluation study; or
>
> - work proved to be of equal value.
>
> The Equality Act 2010 simplified anti-discrimination law by consolidating the Equal Pay Act 1970 and numerous other Acts and Regulations into a single piece of legislation.

In 2011, more women than men worked part-time. To attempt to eliminate the effect that this factor has on the relative pay of men and women, the investigation in this section will only concern men and women working full-time; and this only applies to employees being paid adult rates whose pay was not affected by absence in the pay-period for which the data were collected. Although leaving out part-time workers does make it easier to compare like with like, it also means we have omitted many millions of employees, most of them women, from the comparison.

Note that identifying the relevant variables and deciding on appropriate measures of them is an important aspect of any statistical (and often scientific) investigation.

Before looking at the effect of occupation on pay, we shall first consider any difference between the overall earnings of men and women. Table 1 gives the mean gross (that is, before any deductions, such as tax, pension and national insurance, are removed) weekly earnings of adult men and women in full-time employment in the UK in 2011.

(Note that in this unit all the results from the ASHE 2011 are based on the provisional 2011 data, which was available at the time of writing. The revised 2011 data has since become available; however, the changes are minimal and do not change any conclusions made in this unit.)

Table 1 Mean gross weekly earnings of adult men and women in full-time employment (to the nearest pound)

	Women	Men
Mean	515	658

(Source: *Annual Survey of Hours and Earnings*, 2011, Table 1.1)

Having obtained some data, the next step is to decide how to compare the earnings of men and women. From Table 1, it is clear that the mean gross weekly earnings for men is greater than the corresponding figure for women. Two methods of comparing men's and women's mean earnings might spring to mind: subtracting one from the other to find the (numerical) difference, and dividing one by the other to find the ratio.

First, consider the *absolute* numerical difference: this is £(658 − 515) = £143. So the mean gross weekly earnings of adult men is £143 more than the mean gross weekly earnings for women.

Is this a useful way of comparing the earnings of men and women?

Suppose that the mean weekly earnings of men and women had been £358 and £215, respectively; in this case, the absolute numerical difference would also have been £143, as it would have been if the weekly earnings had been £1658 and £1515. However, an absolute difference of £143 would be regarded as of much greater importance in the first case than in the second. So it would be better to know something about the *relative* size of the difference and not just the *absolute* difference.

In Unit 2, ratios rather than absolute differences were used to compare prices. One of the benefits of using ratios is that whatever the unit of measurement – pounds, pence, euros, dollars – the ratio remains the same. Also, because ratios do not depend on the absolute size of the quantities being compared, only on their relative size, ratios calculated at different times can be meaningfully compared. So using relative comparisons makes it possible to extend the investigation to make international comparisons or to make comparisons over time.

You will use other ratios later.

So let's use earnings *ratios*. Since the available data in Table 1 are the *mean* gross weekly earnings for men and for women, take the ratio of these means first. The technical term for this is the *earnings ratio at the mean*.

> **Earnings ratio at the mean**
>
> This earnings ratio at the mean is defined as:
>
> $$\frac{\text{mean earnings of women}}{\text{mean earnings of men}}.$$

An established convention is to take this ratio as the mean women's earnings divided by the mean men's earnings, rather than the other way round.

Example 1   *Calculating an earnings ratio at the mean*

For the data in Table 1, the earnings ratio at the mean is

$$\frac{515}{658} = 0.782\,6748 = 0.78 \text{ (to two decimal places)}.$$

We shall generally round ratios like this to two decimal places.

In fact, earnings ratios are usually expressed as percentages. Thus, the mean gross weekly earnings of adult women in full-time employment in 2011 was approximately 78% of the mean gross weekly earnings of adult men in full-time employment. (Rounding the ratio to two decimal places corresponds to rounding the percentage to the nearest one per cent.)

Example 1 is the subject of Screencast 1 for Unit 3 (see the M140 website).

> In a context where men usually earn more than women, the earnings ratio at the mean will usually be less than one or, as a percentage, less than 100%. The nearer the earnings ratio at the mean is to 100%, the closer are the 'average' earnings of women to those of men.

Table 1 gives the mean gross weekly earnings of adult men and women in full-time employment. This 'compares like with like' to some extent, by avoiding the effects of part-time work and of being paid on non-adult rates. However, there are other factors that affect earnings, like total hours worked, amount of overtime and occupation. Might any of these factors have an effect on the relative earnings of men and women? If they do, then, in order to make a fair comparison, they should be taken into account. How can you find out what effects they have, and take these into account by excluding them from the comparison? We start by looking at hours worked and overtime. You might expect there could be differences between the hours worked and overtime of men and women.

3. Analyse

Table 2   Mean weekly hours worked by adult men and women in full-time employment in the UK in 2011 (to one decimal place)

	Women	Men
Normal basic	36.8	38.7
Overtime	0.5	1.5
Total	37.4	40.2

(Source: *Annual Survey of Hours and Earnings*, 2011, Tables 1.9, 1.10 and 1.11)

Note that in Table 2 the normal and overtime average hours do not exactly add up to the total average hours for women, because of a discrepancy caused by rounding.

Activity 1   *Hours and overtime*

(a) On average, how many hours did women work per week in 2011? (In this context, interpret the phrase 'on average' as 'using the *mean*'.) Was this more or less than the average number of hours worked by men?

(b) On average, did men or women do more overtime per week in 2011, and by how much?

(c) What do you think the effect would be of excluding overtime pay from the mean gross weekly earnings used to calculate the earnings ratio at the mean? Do you think this earnings ratio would increase or decrease if overtime were excluded?

(d) Men and women worked a different number of hours per week on average. Can you suggest a way of eliminating any effect due to this?

Activity 2   *Calculating earnings ratios*

Table 3   Mean gross weekly and hourly earnings, excluding overtime, of adult men and women

	Women	Men
Mean gross *weekly* earnings excluding overtime (£)	509	635
Mean gross *hourly* earnings excluding overtime (pence)	1382	1643

(Source: *Annual Survey of Hours and Earnings*, 2011, Tables 1.2 and 1.6)

In Example 1, the earnings ratio at the mean based on gross weekly earnings, including overtime, was found to be 78%. Use the data in Table 3 to do the following:

(a) Calculate the earnings ratio at the mean based on gross *weekly* earnings excluding overtime.

(b) Calculate the earnings ratio at the mean based on gross *hourly* earnings excluding overtime.

(c) Describe the effect on the earnings ratio at the mean of excluding overtime and using data for hourly earnings instead of weekly earnings.

As you should have seen in part (c) of Activity 2, the longer average working week and the extra overtime worked by men each account for part of the difference between the weekly earnings of men and women. Therefore, to find out whether or not groups of men and women receive equal pay for a similar amount of work, we need to use gross hourly earnings, excluding overtime (when available), for a fairer comparison.

1.3   The Annual Survey of Hours and Earnings

The data which we use to compare men's and women's earnings in this unit are taken from a government survey called the Annual Survey of Hours and Earnings (ASHE). This annual survey has been carried out by the Office for National Statistics (ONS) each April since 2004. Before that there was a similar survey called the New Earnings Survey, carried out from 1970 to 2003.

The main purpose of the survey is to provide information on patterns of earnings and paid hours for employees within industries, occupations and regions. The survey results are used by the UK government and many other organisations, both public and private. Among other uses, ASHE data are used by the UK government to help set minimum wage levels, and (as we are doing in this unit) to investigate the gender pay-gap.

Currently, ASHE collects information on about 180 000 men and women who are members of the Pay-As-You-Earn (PAYE) scheme. Thus the survey does not cover the self-employed nor, of course, unemployed people. (The survey also omits people whose employer does not employ anyone who earns above the (low) threshold that requires the business to register for PAYE; however, ONS investigations indicate that this omission does not cause a major bias.)

To collect the data, the employer of each selected employee is contacted. The employee is identified by name and National Insurance number and the employer is required, by law, to provide information relating to that employee's earnings during a specified week.

The data collected include (among other things) the following items of information concerning the employee:

- total earnings for the pay-period including the specified week
- location of workplace
- occupation
- information concerning normal basic hours, overtime earnings and hours, bonus payments, pension contributions and length of pay-period.

2. Collect

The employee's age and gender are also recorded from other government sources. This information is analysed by ONS, along with information on national numbers of employees in specific groups taken from another government survey, the Labour Force Survey. (It is this extra information that, among other things, gets round the issue of the omission of employers whose employees all fall below the PAYE threshold.) The results are published online on the ONS website.

1.4   Averages: the mean or the median?

So far you have used the mean when comparing the levels of earnings of men and women. But there are other measures for summarising data: the median, in particular. Would the results of the investigation have been the same using *median* earnings of men and women? You already know from Unit 2 that, as measures of location, the median and the mean differ in important ways – for instance, they differ in their resistance to extreme values in the data. But here let us look at a different aspect, connected to the *skewness* of the data.

The mean earnings of any group of people may be thought of as the 'average' of the earnings of all the people in that group. The median earnings may be thought of as the earnings of the 'middle-income person', or more precisely (as income also includes things other than pay), as the person on middle earnings; that is, if you listed the people in order of their earnings, then the person halfway up the list (and halfway down) gets the median earnings. So mean earnings and median earnings are different ways of measuring the 'middle' level of earnings of the group.

...and I was really shocked to discover that 50% of workers earn less than the median wage

Table 4 gives values of the median and mean gross weekly earnings including and excluding overtime, and the median and mean gross hourly earnings excluding overtime for adult men and women in full-time employment in 2011.

Table 4 Median and mean earnings for men and women in 2011

	Median		Mean	
	Women	Men	Women	Men
Gross weekly earnings incl. overtime (£)	440	538	515	658
Gross weekly earnings excl. overtime (£)	432	509	509	635
Gross hourly earnings excl. overtime (p)	1174	1311	1382	1643

(Source: *Annual Survey of Hours and Earnings*, 2011, Tables 1.1, 1.2 and 1.6)

The *earnings ratio at the median* is defined in a similar way to the earnings ratio at the mean.

Earnings ratio at the median

The earnings ratio at the median is defined as:

$$\frac{\text{median earnings of women}}{\text{median earnings of men}}.$$

Activity 3 *The earnings ratio at the median*

(a) Calculate the earnings ratio at the median using the data in Table 4 for each of the following: gross weekly earnings including overtime, gross weekly earnings excluding overtime, gross hourly earnings excluding overtime.

(b) Compare the three earnings ratios at the median that you calculated in part (a) with the corresponding earnings ratios at the mean (which were calculated in Example 1 and Activity 2). This latter set of values is 78%, 80% and 84%, respectively. What do you notice?

3. Analyse

Activity 3 showed that in each considered case the earnings ratio at the median is greater than the earnings ratio at the mean. Remember, the nearer any earnings ratio is to 100%, the closer the earnings of women are to those of men. So the relative 'gap' between median earnings is less than the relative gap between mean earnings.

Looking again at Table 4, it can also be seen that, for both men and women, the median earnings figure is less than the mean earnings figure. In fact, for earnings data, it is generally true that the median is smaller than the mean. Why should this be so?

Here is an example of a typical *distribution* of earnings; that is, how earnings vary between employees. Imagine a small manufacturing company. The earnings of the majority of the employees will probably not be very different from one another; maybe some will earn as much as twice the amount that others do, but not much more. However, there will almost certainly be one or two senior managers who earn very much more. This hypothetical distribution of earnings is illustrated in Figure 3.

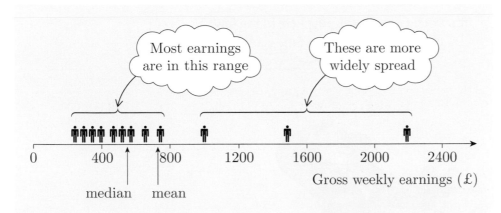

Figure 3   The distribution of earnings in a small (imaginary) company

So the earnings of the majority of employees will be fairly closely grouped, but there will be a few who earn much more. This is the case for earnings in general. This distribution of earnings is the primary reason for the phenomenon that median earnings are generally lower than mean earnings.

To see why this is, imagine that the gross weekly earnings of the highest-paid employee in the imaginary company goes up from about £2200 (as in Figure 3) to £3000. What effect would that have on the median earnings?

The median would not change (if the other pay levels remain unchanged), because however large the highest-paid employee's pay becomes, the middle values remain the same. The mean, however, is the total earnings of the 12 employees divided by 12. So, as the highest-paid employee's pay increases, the total earnings of the 12 employees increases and hence the mean rises. Increasing the highest-paid employee's pay has the effect of dragging up the mean, even if everyone else's pay remains the same.

Since, in general, higher earnings are much more widely spread than lower earnings, this phenomenon of the mean being greater than the median is to be expected when examining earnings data. Further, the more widely spread the higher earnings are, compared with the lower earnings, the greater the difference will be between the mean and the median.

For the earnings data in Table 4, the mean is greater than the median for both men and women. This reflects the fact that higher earnings are more widely spread than lower earnings for both men and women. Also, in Activity 3, you found that the earnings ratio at the median is greater than the earnings ratio at the mean in each case, so the relative gap between median earnings is less than that for mean earnings. This is due to higher earnings being more widely spread, compared with lower earnings, for men than for women.

"It's true, the average pay here is too low. I'll give myself a big pay-rise."

Decisions about which measure to use have implications for how the data are interpreted. Since mean earnings are generally higher than median earnings, a trade union official might use median earnings to support an argument that average pay is low. On the other hand, the employer might use the mean to argue the opposite. As the relatively large earnings of a minority can have a marked effect on mean earnings, whereas the median is unaffected by a few extremely large values, so there is a case for regarding the median as more representative of earnings in general than the mean. For the rest of the investigation into the earnings of men and women here, we shall use the median rather than the mean.

There is, however, nothing *unique* to earnings data that leads to the median being less than the mean. Since this arises from the higher values being more widely spread out than the lower values, it will occur in any data with that characteristic. You know from Units 1 and 2 that data of this kind, where the higher values are more widely spread out than the lower values, are said to be right-skew. So in right-skew data, the median will generally be less than the mean.

What about left-skew data? Well, everything works in the opposite direction. In left-skew data, the lower values are more widely spread out, compared to the higher values, and this leads to the median generally being greater than the mean. These characteristics are summarised below.

Skewness, the median and the mean

In *right-skew* data, the median is generally *less* than the mean.

In *left-skew* data, the median is generally *greater* than the mean.

'Should we scare the opposition by announcing
our mean height or lull them by announcing
our median height?'

The pay parade

The following cartoon appeared in a journal article in 1994. Imagine a
parade of all the workers in the UK, in which everyone's height is
proportional to their weekly earnings: so a person earning an average (that
is, mean) wage is of mean height. The shortest, that is the lowest-paid, is
first in the parade, the tallest, that is the highest-paid, is last. Suppose the
parade takes an hour with everyone moving at the same speed. For the
first 25 minutes all you will see are very short people – nearly ten million
people less than four feet tall. Only in the last 25 minutes do you see
people of average (mean) height, followed by a few giants: government
ministers who are nine metres tall and heads of companies who are as tall
as a skyscraper. (This idea of a 'pay parade' dates back at least to a 1971
publication by the Dutch economist Jan Pen. The figures in the text, but
not the cartoon itself, have been updated to relate to the UK position in
2011.)

(Source: The Low Pay Unit, *The New Review*, No. 24)

Activity 4   *The pay parade: calculations and interpretations*

Suppose that the parade, described above, begins at 10 am and ends at 11 am.

(a) At what time would a person of median earnings pass by?

(b) According to the description of the pay parade, at what time does a person earning the mean wage pass by? How does this relate to the type of skewness in these income data? What percentage of people earn less than the mean wage?

Activity 5   *The pay parade: using images*

Think about the cartoon image itself: what were some of your reactions to it? Were there any aspects that confused you, or where you felt you were being misled?

Though the cartoon provides a powerful image, some images can be misleading! In the cartoon, a person earning twice the average wage is drawn twice as tall as a person earning the average wage. However, that person is also drawn twice as wide – the tall people are not tall and thin – so the *area* of the cartoon taken up by a person earning twice the average wage is *four* (2×2) times the area taken up by a person earning the average wage. And, in practice, a reader may well interpret a person in the cartoon as a figure occupying a *volume* in space. So the impression received is of a figure *eight* ($2 \times 2 \times 2$) times as large. Thus, the effect of the cartoon is to exaggerate the differences in earnings of different people.

Unfortunately, many published diagrams make use of area or volume to exaggerate the visual effect of points they are trying to make. Look out for this whenever you see diagrams used to support an argument.

The cartoon is based on the idea that greater height corresponds to greater income. This choice has quite strong psychological overtones to do with cultural norms of 'stature', 'importance', and so on; it is a far from neutral image. Consider the impact of a redrawn cartoon where the key image was a person with their hand outstretched: the larger the salary, the longer the arm.

One reason you may be able to orientate yourself with regard to the cartoon as it stands, is that you have plenty of experience of the distribution of people's heights and you can use this to interpret the image. Most importantly, there is no scale, other than the notion of 'average height'.

Let's turn away from the pay parade and summarise the investigation so far. Several factors that affect earnings have been taken into account. Since more women than men work part-time, the investigation was restricted to full-time workers. Only workers on adult pay rates were considered. Since men work more overtime on average than women, overtime was excluded. Since the normal basic working week is slightly longer on average for men than for women, the average hourly earnings of men and women were compared instead of the average weekly earnings. Since a few well-paid individuals can strongly influence the mean but not the median, the median was used for comparisons. This is summarised in Table 5.

Table 5 Adjustments made in order to compare 'like with like'

Perceived problem	Proposed solution
More women than men work part-time.	Look only at full-time workers on adult pay rates.
Men work more overtime.	Exclude overtime.
Men work a longer basic working week.	Compare hourly earnings.
A few highly-paid individuals can seriously influence the mean.	Compare median earnings.

Even after taking all these factors into account, the earnings ratio at the median for 2011 was 90%. So it appears that adult women working full-time receive a median hourly rate that is only about 90% of the median hourly rate for men (see Activity 3 earlier in the subsection). Does this mean that women and men are not receiving equal pay for equal work? Or are there other aspects that have not yet been taken into account?

Perhaps the most important factor influencing pay that has not yet been considered, is actual occupation; one aspect of this is briefly investigated later in the unit.

We have seen that looking at data on hourly (rather than weekly) pay has advantages. However, particularly when looking at individual occupations, there are disadvantages too. In many occupations, there is no paid overtime: pay is based on a nominal number of contracted hours and is fixed regardless of the number of hours actually worked, so that the published figure for hourly earnings may bear little relationship with reality. This is the case in many professions.

In secondary-school teaching, for example, the basic working week for full-time workers according to the results of the ASHE is a little over 32 hours. However, this relates only to 'directed' hours of work, and teachers are expected (and indeed required, under their contracts of employment) to carry out other duties, such as much of their lesson preparation and marking, outside these hours. Indeed, many surveys have established that secondary-school teachers work, on average, many more hours in a week than the 32 in their basic working week, generally without any extra pay. But ASHE data on hourly pay do not take into account these extra working hours. In such occupations, ASHE figures for hourly earnings are fairly meaningless and should certainly not be used for comparisons with earnings in other occupations.

Taking all these factors into account, the module team settled for using data on weekly earnings excluding overtime for most comparisons in M140.

Another important aspect is that, so far, the only features of the pay distribution that we have considered are its mean and median. In the next subsection, other features are considered. In terms of the pay parade, we ask whether there are ways in which the numbers of men and women vary towards the start and end of the parade, rather than in the middle.

1.5 Deciles

You have seen data on median and mean pay from ASHE, for various groups of workers. But the ASHE results do not provide only means and medians. For instance, Table 6 shows the data presented in the 2011 ASHE report on gross weekly pay excluding overtime, for male and female workers separately. (The data are for workers on adult rates of pay, whose pay was not affected by absence.) To begin with, we'll concentrate on the data for male workers.

Table 6 Weekly pay excluding overtime (rounded to the nearest £) for full-time employee jobs in the UK, 2011

Percentile	Female	Male
10	253	284
20	296	340
25	316	364
30	335	390
40	380	446
60	497	581
70	574	676
75	619	738
80	671	813
90	820	1083
Median	432	509
Mean	509	635

(Source: *Annual Survey of Hours and Earnings*, 2011, Table 1.2)

Well, you know what the median and mean are, but what about all these 'percentiles'?

You are already familiar with the idea of the quartiles of a batch of data 'cutting' the batch into quarters. That is, when the numbers in the batch are sorted into order, one quarter of the values are below the lower quartile, and one quarter are above the upper quartile. Percentiles are a related idea. According to the data for male workers in Table 6, the percentile labelled 10 for these data is £284. This quantity is usually called the *10th percentile*, and what it means (in this case) is that 10% of men in 2011 earned less than the 10th percentile, that is, less than £284 a week. Similarly, for these data, the 20th percentile is £340, which means that 20% of men earned less than £340 per week.

In general the nth **percentile** is the number such that n% of the values in the batch fall below it.

Activity 6 *Percentiles in the ASHE*

(a) Most of the percentiles in Table 6 correspond to a percentage that is a multiple of 10. However, two of them, the 25th and the 75th percentile, are not multiples of 10. Why do you think these two percentiles are included? What is the other name for these two percentiles?

(b) The table does not give the zeroth or the 100th percentile – these would be the extremes (the maximum and minimum) of the dataset. Apart from that, the column of the table labelled 'Percentile' gives all the percentiles corresponding to a percentage that is a multiple of 10, *except* the 50th percentile. Why is that one omitted? (Hint: it appears elsewhere in the table.)

So Activity 6 explains that some percentiles are the same as quantities for which there is another name. The 25th percentile is the lower quartile, the 75th percentile is the upper quartiles, and the 50th percentile is the median.

> ### Deciles
>
> Percentiles for which the corresponding percentage is a multiple of 10 also have another name: **deciles**. This is because they divide up the batch of data into tenths.
>
> One tenth of the values are below the 10th percentile, one tenth are between the 10th and the 20th percentiles, and so on. In particular, the 10th percentile is called the **lowest decile** and the 90th percentile is called the **highest decile**.

'Decile' comes from the Latin word 'decem', which means 'ten'.

The lowest and highest deciles of a batch of data help us to investigate what are known as the *tails* of its distribution. Just as the quartiles cut off the extreme quarters, or 25%, at either end, the highest decile cuts off the top 10% whilst the lowest decile cuts off the bottom 10%. Figure 4 illustrates these and other key positions we have seen so far (excluding the mean).

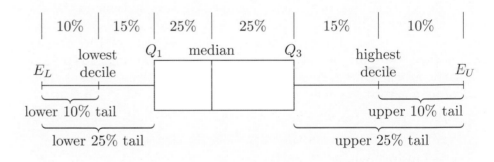

Figure 4   Extremes, lowest and highest deciles, quartiles and median

---

Example 2   *Interpreting some special percentiles*

4. Interpret

If you look at the figures for male workers in Table 6, you can see that the median earnings of males on adult rates in full-time employment (whose pay was not affected by absence) was £509 (rounded to the nearest pound). This means that, in a week, 50% of this group of men earned more than £509 whilst 50% earned less than £509. The upper and lower quartiles for men, given in Table 6, are 738 and 364, so 25% of this group earned less than £364, whilst 50% earned between £364 and £738, and 25% earned more than £738. The extra information we obtain by looking at the highest decile, 1083, and the lowest decile, 284, is that only 10% of this group earned more than £1083 and only 10% earned less than £284. Recall that we are not told what the extreme values are.

You learned in the last unit why a boxplot is a useful diagrammatic representation of a batch of data. It could therefore be informative to draw a boxplot of the data in Table 6. However, we cannot draw a boxplot exactly like those in Unit 2 since there we marked the extremes of the batch, E_L and E_U, on the boxplot and we do not know the extremes of this batch.

It is quite common, when dealing with large batches of data from surveys like the ASHE, not to know the extreme values. So we often draw a boxplot which extends only from the lowest decile to the highest decile. A boxplot like this is called a **decile boxplot**.

Example 3   *A decile boxplot*

Figure 5 shows a decile boxplot of the weekly earnings of the group of adult male full-time employees discussed in Example 2. Arrowheads are used at the end of the whiskers, to remind us that these points represent the highest and lowest deciles and *not* the extremes.

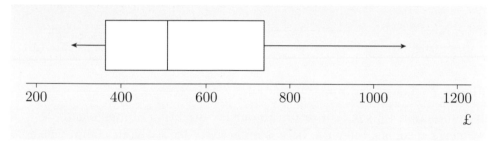

Figure 5   Decile boxplot of weekly earnings for male full-time employees

---

Example 3 is the subject of Screencast 2 for Unit 3 (see the M140 website).

When you have a batch of data, large or small, you will be, for many purposes, most interested in investigating the main body of the data; that is, the part in the middle of the distribution that contains the most typical data values. For example, you might often look just at the median and the quartiles. However, studying the more extreme values that are far from the median – the **tails** of the distribution – is often also important, as you will see later in this module. This method of describing the tails by giving the highest and lowest deciles can be very useful. Indeed, it is common to go further out into the tails and look for the points that separate off the top and bottom 5% of the values, or further still to *cut off* the top and bottom 2.5%, 1% or 0.5%.

As with the deciles and quartiles, the end parts of the distribution that are cut off are called the 5% tails, or the 2.5% tails, or the 1% tails, or the 0.5% tails. Some of these tails are shown in Figures 6 and 7.

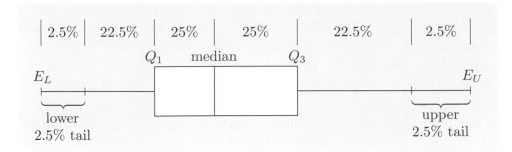

Figure 6   Lower and upper 2.5% tails

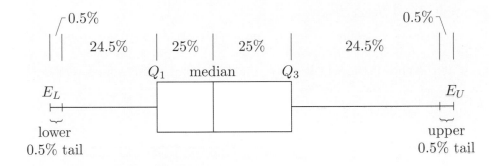

Figure 7   Lower and upper 0.5% tails

In Subsection 1.6 we shall return to our investigation of men's and women's earnings, but first, here is an activity to test your comprehension of the ASHE data that we shall be using, and of the various ways you have met to describe the data.

Activity 7   *Extracting information from a table of percentiles*

These questions concern the group of male full-time employees on adult rates included in Table 6. ASHE, the source for these data, also informs us that the number of employees in this group (in the UK as a whole, not in the actual sample) was estimated as 10 652 000.

(a) What percentage of the men in this group earned more than £1083 in that week?

(b) What percentage of the men in this group earned between £284 and £509 in that week?

(c) Approximately how many men in this group earned less than £364 in that week?

1.6   Earnings ratios across the distribution

Let us now return to our investigation comparing men's and women's earnings. We have dealt with many aspects of the need to compare like with like. As mentioned earlier, there is a need for compromise in this regard, and Table 5 (in Subsection 1.4) re-emphasises this. That table does not include several factors that Figure 2 (in Subsection 1.1) identifies as affecting earnings (educational background is one example). Also, we have not yet considered how to take into account different occupations. However, other variables have been taken into account; for instance:

1. Pose

- age (to the limited extent of considering only those on adult rates of pay)

- hours worked (full-time or part-time)

- absentees (those whose pay for the survey pay-period was affected by absence).

In order to compare like with like we shall, in this subsection, compare only employees who are:

- on adult rates of pay

- full-time

- non-absentees.

We shall also exclude overtime pay. The question of whether to use weekly or hourly pay was also raised in the text below Table 5 – there are pros and cons, but for the rest of this section we shall use weekly pay.

Table 6 thus contains the relevant data for making the comparison for 2011. For convenience, here is the table again, but giving only the data that will be most relevant for our purposes. These are the figures for the highest decile (90th percentile), the upper quartile (75th percentile), the median (50th percentile, though it is not labelled in that way in Table 6),the lower quartile (25th percentile), and the lowest decile (10th percentile).

2. Collect

Table 7   Weekly pay excluding overtime (rounded to the nearest £) for full-time employee jobs in the UK, 2011

	Female	Male
Highest decile	820	1083
Upper quartile	619	738
Median	432	509
Lower quartile	316	364
Lowest decile	253	284

(Source: *Annual Survey of Hours and Earnings*, 2011, Table 1.2)

You have already calculated (in Activity 3 of Subsection 1.4) the earnings ratio at the median for these data: it was 85%. However, that compares only the 'average workers' in the middle of the earnings distribution. Just as for the median (and the mean), earnings ratios at the quartiles and the deciles can be defined.

Earnings ratios at the quartiles and deciles

The **earnings ratio at the lower quartile** is:

$$\frac{\text{lower quartile earnings of women}}{\text{lower quartile earnings of men}}.$$

The **earnings ratio at the lowest decile** is:

$$\frac{\text{lowest decile earnings of women}}{\text{lowest decile earnings of men}}.$$

The **earnings ratio at the upper quartile** is:

$$\frac{\text{upper quartile earnings of women}}{\text{upper quartile earnings of men}}.$$

The **earnings ratio at the highest decile** is:

$$\frac{\text{highest decile earnings of women}}{\text{highest decile earnings of men}}.$$

3. Analyse

Activity 8   *Calculating earnings ratios*

Calculate the earnings ratios at the upper quartile, the lower quartile, the highest decile and the lowest decile, for the workers represented in Table 7. (Round your answers to the nearest one per cent.)

4. Interpret

To make sense of all these ratios, it is helpful to put them in the order that the various percentiles would come in a batch of data, as in Table 8.

Table 8   Earnings ratios at a range of percentiles

Percentile	Earnings ratio
Highest decile	76%
Upper quartile	84%
Median	85%
Lower quartile	87%
Lowest decile	89%

At the bottom end of the distribution the earnings ratio is rather higher than at the top end, and the earnings ratio at the highest decile is quite a lot lower than the others. However, the figures indicate that the earnings ratio does not vary too much across the range from the lowest decile to the highest decile. As an overall summary of these figures we can reasonably say that the earnings ratio is about 85%.

In Figure 8, the decile boxplots for the earnings of both the men and women in Table 7 have been drawn on the same scale.

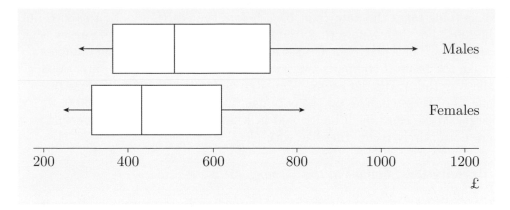

Figure 8 Decile boxplots comparing earnings of men and women

Although there is some degree of overlap between these two boxplots, it is clear that the location of the distribution for males exceeds that for females by quite a margin. Each of the five values plotted (median, quartiles, deciles) for the males is quite a distance to the right (higher on the scale) than the corresponding figure for the females. That is, there still remained a considerable difference between the pay levels for men and women in the UK in 2011.

1.7 Has the 'gap' between men's and women's earnings been closing?

Now that we have a method of comparing earnings, we can return to our question about how the gap between men's and women's pay has changed over the last 15 or so years. We shall return from looking at weekly earnings, to looking at hourly earnings – this is simply because hourly earnings (excluding overtime) for previous years are easier to find! Table 9 shows the median gross hourly earnings, excluding overtime, for adult employees for the years 1997 to 2011.

1. Pose

Table 9 Median gross hourly earnings excluding overtime (in pence)

Year	Women	Men
1997	694	840
1998	722	874
1999	758	907
2000	783	935
2001	823	984
2002	867	1026
2003	904	1058
2004	937	1096
2005	982	1129
2006	1023	1171
2007	1048	1197
2008	1092	1250
2009	1139	1297
2010	1169	1300
2011	1174	1311

(Source: *Patterns of Pay*, 1997 to 2011 ASHE Results, 2011, Table 1)

This table takes the data right back before the ASHE was first carried out in 2004. For data before that, the source is the New Earnings Survey, the predecessor of ASHE, but ONS statisticians have adjusted the numbers to make the basis of comparison between the surveys more accurate. Also, the way the ASHE data were calculated changed in 2006, although the effects of these changes on the earnings ratio is not thought to be too large. These effects will be ignored in what follows, although it means we are not entirely comparing like with like.

Activity 9   *Changes in the earnings ratio over time*

(a) Calculate the earnings ratio at the median for each year in Table 9.

(b) How has the earnings ratio changed since 1997?

(c) On the evidence of your calculations, would you say that gender inequalities in earnings have widened, narrowed or stayed the same between 1997 and 2011?

3. Analyse

In conclusion, certainly there have been changes in the earnings ratio at the median over the 15-year period considered. Over this period, the median pay of female employees did move closer to that of male employees, on an hourly basis at least. But the increase, while steady, has been rather slow, and on this measure, women in 2011 were still earning rather less than men. But we have not been able to investigate all the possible reasons for this discrepancy, and indeed several of the reasons cannot be investigated using ASHE data alone.

4. Interpret

The next subsection contains a brief investigation of one other aspect of the difference between men's and women's earnings: the effect of different occupations.

1.8 Further investigations into gender and earnings

Figure 2 (in Subsection 1.1) pictured many factors, in addition to gender, that influence earnings. It is quite possible that it is really these other factors, such as educational background and type of job, which are the basic causes of the difference between men's and women's earnings. So in this subsection we shall briefly consider how an investigation into the influences of such other factors might proceed.

1. Pose

For example, one possibility is that the lower earnings of women are due largely to the types of job that they do. The ASHE provides information on the earnings of people in different occupations, and these are the kind of data that are needed to investigate this possibility. As an illustration of one method of starting such an investigation, the distribution of the earnings of men and women in public and private sector jobs is summarised in Table 10. The table excludes some occupations that are not classified as being in either the public sector or in the private sector.

2. Collect

Table 10 Distribution of gross weekly earnings (excluding overtime) of full-time adults in the public and private sectors, 2011 (rounded to the nearest £)

| | Public | | Private | |
	Men	Women	Men	Women
Highest decile	1065	844	1095	791
Upper quartile	781	675	709	543
Median	588	510	480	372
Lower quartile	429	377	347	282
Lowest decile	341	307	274	235

(Source: *Annual Survey of Hours and Earnings*, 2011, Table 13.2)

Activity 10   *Comparing earnings ratios*

Use the data in Table 10 to calculate the earnings ratio at each point for both public sector and private sector occupations. (Round your answers to the nearest one per cent.)

Compare these ratios with the figures for all full-time workers, calculated in Activities 3 and 8, which were: highest decile 76%, upper quartile 84%, median 85%, lower quartile 87% and lowest decile 89%. What do you notice?

3. Analyse

We can also draw decile boxplots for all four of the batches of data described by Table 10.

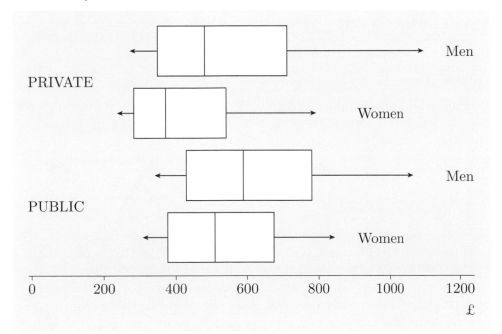

Figure 9 Decile boxplots comparing male and female earnings in the private and public sectors

Comparing the boxplots in Figure 9, you can see that, for both men and women (except the highest-paid men), earnings are lower in the private sector than in the public sector, but the difference is markedly greater for women than for men.

Calculating the earnings ratios of public and private sector employees has not, by itself, given us any clear evidence about the relationship between types of job and the comparison of women's and men's earnings. Now, the public and private categories are themselves composed of a variety of occupations, but, as can be seen from the examples in the next activity, even if we look at more specific occupations, the only consistent pattern that emerges is that women earn less than men.

Activity 11   *Comparing earnings ratios for different occupations*

Table 11 gives the median and quartiles (rounded to the nearest pound) of the distribution of the gross weekly earnings of full-time adult men and women in a variety of occupations.

Table 11   Gross weekly earnings for a variety of occupations

Occupation:	Sales and retail assistants			Secondary education professionals			Kitchen and catering assistants			Managers and directors in retail/wholesale		
	M	W	R	M	W	R	M	W	R	M	W	R
Upper quartile	352	312		852	801		297	283		698	497	
Median	289	260		737	699		247	245		502	374	
Lower quartile	248	227		624	560		216	213		383	302	

M: Men   W: Women   R: Earnings ratio

(Source: *Annual Survey of Hours and Earnings*, 2011, Table 14.2)

Calculate all the earnings ratios (rounded to the nearest one per cent) and complete the 'R' columns. How do the earnings ratios compare across these occupations?

Statisticians' earnings

Statisticians are in an occupation category that has median weekly earnings of £849 for men and £707 for women. These are higher than the medians for other occupations in Table 11. Probably the underlying reason, unfortunately, is that management consultants, actuaries and economists are the other groups in the category containing statisticians.

We have now explored enough aspects of gender difference in earnings to conclude that women do still earn less than men, by several different measures, although the overall position is complicated and we have not been able to investigate all the potentially important factors.

In Section 2, we move away from gender comparisons, and look more generally at boxplots.

Exercises on Section 1

Exercise 1   *Interpreting a percentile*

There are 10 652 000 men in the group represented in Table 6 (in Subsection 1.5). How many of them earned £813 or more in that week?

Table 6 is repeated below for convenience.

Percentile	Female	Male
10	253	284
20	296	340
25	316	364
30	335	390
40	380	446
60	497	581
70	574	676
75	619	738
80	671	813
90	820	1083
Median	432	509
Mean	509	635

(Source: *Annual Survey of Hours and Earnings*, 2011, Table 1.2)

Exercise 2   *Numerical labelling of a decile boxplot*

Figure 10 shows a decile boxplot of the group of female workers in Table 6.

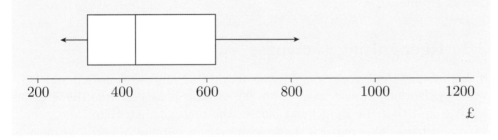

Figure 10   Decile boxplot for female workers

Identify which figures from Table 6 should go by the relevant places on the boxplot to represent the highest and lowest deciles, the quartiles, Q_1 and Q_3, and the median.

Exercise 3   *Earnings ratios in the construction industry*

As well as providing information on the earnings of people in different occupations, ASHE also gives data on earnings in different industries. Table 12 gives some percentiles of weekly pay, excluding overtime, for male and female workers on adult rates of pay in the construction industry.

Table 12   Weekly pay excluding overtime (rounded to the nearest £) for full-time employee jobs in the construction industry in the UK, 2011

	Female	Male
Highest decile	767	966
Upper quartile	575	689
Median	420	507
Lower quartile	326	401
Lowest decile	277	320

(Source: *Annual Survey of Hours and Earnings*, 2011, Table 4.2)

Calculate the earnings ratios at the deciles, quartiles and median for these data. (Round your answers to the nearest one per cent.) Comment on how the earnings ratios differ across the distribution of earnings.

2 Boxplots and skewness

Subsection 2.1 looks again, briefly, at the skewness of distributions and explores further how skewness is represented and recognised in boxplots. Subsection 2.2 covers some details of drawing boxplots that you have not previously met.

2.1 Recognising skewness

If you look at the boxplots in Figures 8 and 9 (in Subsections 1.6 and 1.8) you can see that, in each case, the right whisker is longer than the left whisker and that the right-hand part of the box is longer than the left-hand part. This pattern is very common in batches of earnings data and, as you know, we describe it by saying that the distribution of earnings data is right-skew.

Let us summarise the ways you have already seen in Units 1 and 2 for recognising skewness. A skew distribution is one which is not symmetric, usually because it has one tail longer than the other. Here is a list of characteristics of a batch of data that can be used to recognise skewness.

- The outline of a stemplot: typical shapes are shown in Figure 11.

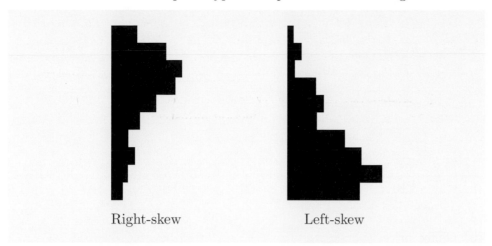

Figure 11 Stemplot shapes

- The whiskers of a boxplot: a long whisker indicates a long tail (though you need to take account of the fact that some of the extreme points might be shown separately on the boxplot).

- The box of the boxplot: in a right-skew batch, the right-hand part of the box (above the median) is longer than the left-hand part of the box (below the median).

Figure 12 Skewness in boxplots

In the following activity, you will get some practice in using the last two of these characteristics to recognise and describe skewness in batches of data. The activity will also serve as a reminder on how boxplots are constructed, as preparation for looking in more detail at the process of drawing boxplots in the next subsection.

Activity 12 *Sketching boxplots and recognising skewness*

The following five-figure summaries are based on data used in Units 1 and 2. For each batch, sketch its boxplot above the scale provided. (Draw the whiskers going right out to the extremes, for these sketches. For this activity, there is no need to draw them particularly carefully.) Say if a batch is left-skew or right-skew, where appropriate.

(a) Arithmetic scores data

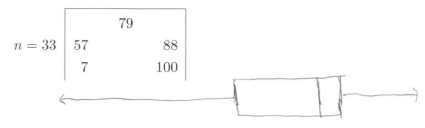

$$n = 33 \quad \begin{array}{|cc|} \hline & 79 & \\ 57 & & 88 \\ 7 & & 100 \\ \hline \end{array}$$

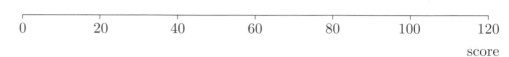

0   20   40   60   80   100   120

score

(b) Coffee prices (pence)

$$n = 15 \quad \begin{array}{|cc|} \hline & 295 & \\ 268 & & 299 \\ 268 & & 369 \\ \hline \end{array}$$

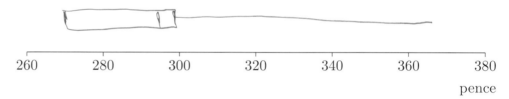

260   280   300   320   340   360   380

pence

(c) Electricity prices (pence per kWh)

$$n = 15 \quad \begin{array}{|cc|} \hline & 13.17 & \\ 12.84 & & 13.83 \\ 12.64 & & 15.03 \\ \hline \end{array}$$

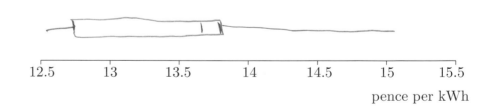

12.5   13   13.5   14   14.5   15   15.5

pence per kWh

You have now covered the material related to Screencast 3 for Unit 3 (see the M140 website).

2.2 Boxplots: the details

In Subsection 3.3 of Unit 2, you learned about boxplots, and you have since seen several of them in that unit and this one. However, apart from the sketches you were asked to produce in Activity 12, you have not actually been asked to produce any boxplots yourself. You will learn how to do so using Minitab in Section 4. First we give some details, that have not been noted earlier, about the way boxplots are constructed.

You know that the central 'box' of the boxplot shows the positions of the quartiles and the median. But in the boxplots you saw in Unit 2, the whiskers sometimes went all the way out to the extremes, and sometimes they did not. How is the choice made on how far the whiskers should go? In very broad terms, the lengths of the whiskers depend on how spread out the more extreme values in the batch of data are, compared to the interquartile range of the batch.

Figure 13   A boxplot with whiskers

Adjacent values

In a boxplot, the whiskers are drawn outwards as far as observations called *adjacent values*.

The **lower adjacent value** is the lowest data value that is within one and a half times the interquartile range of the lower quartile (the lower-end of the box).

The **upper adjacent value** is the highest data value that is within one and a half times the interquartile range of the upper quartile (the upper-end of the box).

To understand exactly how this works, it is easiest to look at an example.

You first met these data in Activity 1 in Unit 2.

Example 4   *Television prices: completing the boxplot*

Figure 14 shows a stemplot of the prices of small flat-screen televisions. These data came up several times in Unit 2 and you worked with a boxplot of the batch in Subsection 2.1.

```
0 | 9
1 | 0
1 | 2 3 3 3
1 | 4 5 5 5 5
1 | 6 6 7
1 | 8 8 9
2 |
2 |
2 | 4 5
2 | 7
```

$$n = 20 \quad 0 \,|\, 9 \text{ represents } £90$$

Figure 14   Prices of all flat-screen televisions with a screen size of 24 inches or less on a major UK retailer's website on a day in February 2012

For these data, the median is 150 and the quartiles are $Q_3 = 180$ and $Q_1 = 130$, so that the interquartile range is $\text{IQR} = 180 - 130 = 50$.

To find the lower adjacent value, first calculate

$$Q_1 - 1.5 \times \text{IQR} = 130 - 1.5 \times 50 = 130 - 75 = 55.$$

The lowest data value, 90, is greater than this, so the lower adjacent value is 90 and the left-hand whisker on the boxplot extends as far as 90.

Similarly, for the upper adjacent value, first calculate

$$Q_3 + 1.5 \times \text{IQR} = 180 + 1.5 \times 50 = 180 + 75 = 255.$$

The highest data value that does not exceed 255 is 250, so the upper adjacent value is 250, and hence the right-hand whisker on the boxplot extends as far as 250. (Note that it does *not* go all the way to 255, only to the upper adjacent value, the highest value not exceeding 255 in the data. Note also that there is a data value, 270 in this case, that is *above* the upper adjacent value.)

Therefore, the boxplot (not yet complete) with the box and the whiskers looks as in Figure 15.

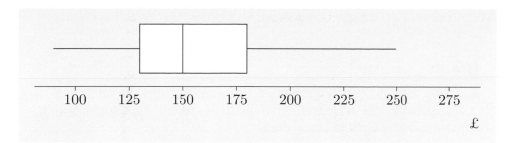

Figure 15 Incomplete boxplot of batch of 20 television prices

The final step is to mark separately any data values that are not covered by the whiskers. In some cases, these may be outliers that do not fit the general pattern of the rest of the batch. In other cases, this is not true, but they are at least *potential* outliers, and the boxplot draws attention to them by plotting them separately.

In these data, there is only one data value not covered by the whiskers, and it is the maximum value, 270. So the resulting boxplot, which you have already seen in Unit 2 (where it was Figure 19 in Subsection 3.3), is shown in Figure 16.

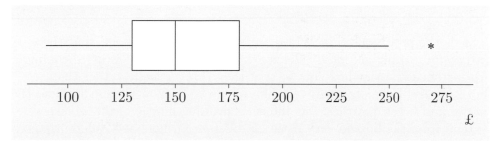

Figure 16 Completed boxplot of batch of 20 television prices

Example 4 is the subject of Screencast 4 for Unit 3 (see the M140 website).

The process of drawing a boxplot can be summarised as follows.

Drawing boxplots

1. The scale for the boxplot must run at least from the minimum to the maximum value in the batch. In M140, the boxplot is drawn so that the scale is horizontal.

2. The 'box' of the boxplot runs from the lower quartile to the upper quartile. Within the box there is a line showing the position of the median.

3. The 'whiskers' of the boxplot are lines, drawn parallel to the scale, that run from the lower quartile to the lower adjacent value, and from the upper quartile to the upper adjacent value. The lower/upper adjacent value is the furthest data value that is within one and a half times the IQR (interquartile range) of the lower/upper quartile.

4. Any individual data values that are not covered by the box or the whiskers are plotted separately (in line with the whiskers). They are potential outliers.

This is the process used in M140, but you must bear in mind that there are no universally accepted rules for drawing boxplots. It is quite common, for instance, to draw boxplots so that they run vertically rather than horizontally. Boxplots always (or almost always!) show the median and the upper and lower quartiles, but the rules defining how long the whiskers extend from the box do vary between different authors and different pieces of software. The approach given here is one of the simplest versions, and is also probably the most common. It is also the approach used by Minitab.

There are many variations on the general boxplot theme – for example you have already come upon decile boxplots, and Figure 17 shows a rather more complicated version of some decile boxplots, taken from the 2011 ONS report on the ASHE results. Here the boxplots run vertically, the boxes are shaded, and different symbols (defined at the side) are used for the median, quartiles and deciles.

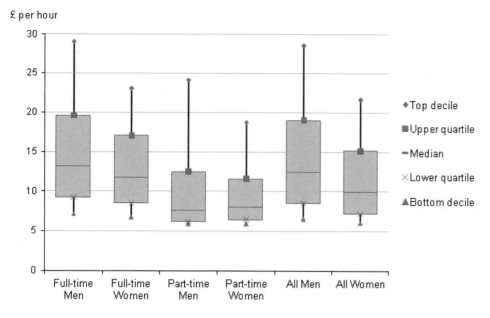

£ per hour

Figure 17   Decile boxplots comparing the hourly earnings of different groups of employees in the UK

(Source: ONS (2012) *2011 Annual Survey of Hours and Earnings (based on SOC 2010)*, p. 9)

You will learn how to use Minitab to produce boxplots in Section 4. But it is worth drawing one or two by hand, to consolidate your understanding of what the different parts mean.

Activity 13   *Boxplots of earnings data*

The stemplot in Figure 18 gives data on the hourly earnings of 40 female full-time employees in the UK. (These are not real data, but were simulated using a computer on the basis of the distribution of earnings (excluding overtime) for this category from the ASHE 2011 results. However, you should not assume that every feature of this batch of data matches the national figures!)

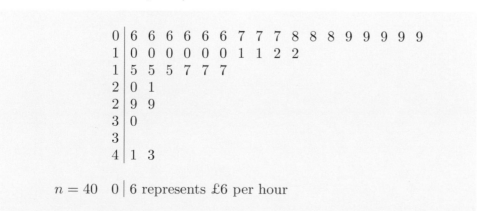

```
0 | 6  6  6  6  6  6  7  7  7  8  8  8  9  9  9  9  9
1 | 0  0  0  0  0  0  1  1  2  2
1 | 5  5  5  7  7  7
2 | 0  1
2 | 9  9
3 | 0
3 |
4 | 1  3
```

n = 40   0 | 6 represents £6 per hour

Figure 18   Stemplot of earnings for 40 female employees

(a) Prepare a five-figure summary of the data in Figure 18.

(b) Find the upper and lower adjacent values for these data. Use them, together with the values you calculated for the five-figure summary in (a), to draw a boxplot for the data in Figure 18.

One of the things you looked at in the previous activity was the spread of a batch of data. In the next section, we return to ways of measuring spread.

Exercises on Section 2

Exercise 4   *Extracting numbers required for a boxplot from a stemplot*

Figure 19 is a stemplot of hourly earnings data for 35 men, generated in a similar way to those for the women in Figure 18.

```
0 | 6  6  7  7  7  7  7  8  8  8  9  9
1 | 0  0  1  1  1  2  3  3  4
1 | 5  5  5  6  6  7  8  9
2 | 1  3  4  4
2 | 9
3 |
3 | 8
```

$n = 35$ $0 \,|\, 6$ represents £6 per hour

Figure 19   Stemplot of earnings for 35 male employees

(a) Find the median and quartiles for these data.

(b) What are the upper and lower adjacent values for the data in Figure 19? Which data values, if any, should be plotted separately on a boxplot?

Exercise 5 *A boxplot for petrol consumption data*

Figure 20 appeared in Unit 1, and is a stemplot of data on petrol consumption for a particular car.

```
        26 | 1  7  9
        27 |
        28 | 1  6
        29 | 6  7
        30 | 1
        31 | 7
        32 | 1  6
        33 | 5
        34 | 1
        35 | 0  2  2  3  3  7  8
        36 | 0  2  3  4  5  7
        37 | 5
        38 | 1  7  8
        39 | 1  3
        40 | 5
        41 |
        42 | 1
```

$n = 34$ 26 | 1 represents 26.1 miles per gallon

Figure 20 Stemplot of the petrol consumption data from Unit 1

(a) Find the median and quartiles for these data.

(b) What are the upper and lower adjacent values for the data in Figure 20? Which data values, if any, should be plotted separately on a boxplot?

(c) Draw a boxplot of the data in Figure 20. Comment on the skewness of this batch of data.

3 Comparing batches

In this section we return to ways of comparing batches of data. We will do this by considering **summary measures**, which are quantities that summarise aspects of a batch of data, such as its location or its spread. You have already spent some time in previous units working on measures of location, and comparing data in terms of these measures. In Section 2 of this unit, you saw some informal ways of looking at and comparing skewness. In this section, however, we concentrate mostly on the spread of a batch of data and introduce a new measure of spread called the *standard deviation*. This is based on measuring the distances of the data values from the mean of the batch. Subsection 3.2 takes a slight detour, looking at how to calculate the mean and standard deviation for data presented in one form of summary table.

3.1 The standard deviation

This company was first mentioned in Unit 2.

The need to compare batches of data, including looking at their spread, has arisen at our mythical software company, Gradgrind Ltd. The programmers are complaining that they are poorly paid compared to the other staff. Have a look at the data in Table 13 for a few minutes before doing Activity 14. Is their claim justified?

Table 13 Gross weekly earnings (£) of employees of Gradgrind Ltd in April 2011

Programmers	Others
465	346
484	376
620	391
654	391
855	415
858	465
	830
	843
	876
	1627

We can begin investigating this question by looking at summary measures of locations and spread that you already know how to calculate.

Activity 14 *Calculating some summary measures*

Treating the programmers as one batch and 'others' as a second batch, for each of these batches find the following:

(a) the mean   (b) the median   (c) the interquartile range.

In Activity 14, you calculated the following two different measures of overall location.

- The mean: the two batches have the same mean (£656).

- The median: the median earnings of the programmers (£637) is higher than that of the other staff (£440).

In both cases, the median is less than the mean, which, as you know from earlier in the unit, typically happens in right-skew batches.

You have also calculated the following measure of spread.

- The interquartile range: the other staff earnings have a slightly higher IQR (£464) than that of the programmers' earnings (£377).

Now we shall introduce another measure of spread: the standard deviation. This measure of spread is related to the mean in the same way that the interquartile range is related to the median – by the method of calculation. Both the median and the IQR are found by ordering the data and finding the values at a particular position (or between two particular positions) of the ordered list of values. The standard deviation, on the other hand, is found by doing calculations similar to those used in calculating the mean: finding sums and dividing by the batch size (or something similar to the batch size).

The basic idea is to calculate a numerical measure that reflects how much the data values spread out or, more precisely, how much the x values spread away from the 'centre' of the batch. We shall represent the 'centre' of a batch by the mean, $\overline{x}$

The deviation

For each data value in a batch we have a **deviation of the data value from the mean**, or just **deviation** for short. If we have a data value x, and the batch mean is $\overline{x}$, then the deviation is $x - \overline{x}$.

As a simple example, suppose a batch consists of just five data: 6, 7, 2, 6 and 4. Then the mean of the batch equals

$$\frac{6 + 7 + 2 + 6 + 4}{5} = 5.$$

Taking 5 from each data value, the first deviation is $6 - 5 = 1$ and the others are 2, -3, 1 and -1.

The size of the deviation

The deviations measure how far the data values in a batch are from the batch mean.

- If a data value is exactly equal to the mean, then the deviation will be zero.

- If a data value is close to the mean, then the deviation will be a small number, near zero.

- If a data value is a long way above the mean, then the deviation will be large and positive.

- If a data value is a long way below the mean, then the deviation will be large and negative.

Thus if a batch has a large spread, its data values will tend to be a relatively long way away from the mean, so the deviations will tend to be large in size. (Large negative numbers and large positive numbers are both large in size.)

The *standard* deviation, as you will see, is just a kind of average deviation – so it will be larger in batches that are more spread out. However, there is an awkward aspect – the deviations have signs, that is, some are positive and some are negative. If all we are interested in is how far the data values are from the batch mean, then the sign is not very interesting. A value 10 units *below* the mean is just as far away from the mean as a value 10 units *above* the mean, so in looking at the spread of the batch, these values should be treated in the same way even though one has a deviation of -10 and the other of 10.

There is more than one way to get round this sign issue, but the one used in calculating the standard deviation is to *square* the deviations. Think again of two data values that have deviations -10 and 10. If these deviations are squared, the squared deviations are both 100 (because the square of a negative number is positive). So squaring them means that the issue of the signs is dealt with.

Activity 15   *Calculating the sum of squared deviations*

Table 14 shows the data values for the programmers, as given originally in Table 13. The first column is completed, and gives all the data values. The mean of these values, $\overline{x}$, is 656. The second column is also completed, and gives this batch mean (which is the same for the whole batch, of course). The entries in the other two columns are not complete. The third column gives the deviation corresponding to each data value, and the deviation for the first data point is filled in as -191. This was calculated from $x - \overline{x} = 465 - 656 = -191$. The fourth column gives the squared deviations. It is again completed only for the first data point, with $(-191)^2 = 36\,481$.

Table 14   Sum of squared deviations

Data x	Mean $\overline{x}$	Deviation $(x - \overline{x})$	Squared deviation $(x - \overline{x})^2$
465	656	−191	36 481
484	656		
620	656		
654	656		
855	656		
858	656		
Σ			

Complete the table by calculating the remaining values for the third and fourth columns, followed by the sum of each of these columns.

In Activity 15, the sum of the deviations was zero. This also happened with our first simple example, where the data values were 6, 7, 2, 6, 4 with deviations 1, 2, −3, 1, −1 (and $1 + 2 - 3 + 1 - 1 = 0$). In fact this will always happen, because there will always be some values below the mean (negative deviations) and some above (positive deviations), and because of the way the mean is calculated: the positives and negatives will always exactly cancel out, giving a zero sum. (That is another reason why we cannot just use the average deviation as a measure of spread.)

However, the sum of the *squared* deviations is not zero, and we could compare batches in terms of spread by looking at this sum – or better, by looking at the *mean* of the squared deviations in a batch. However, there is a small extra complication here. For the programmers, there are six squared deviations, so you might expect to calculate the mean by dividing the sum of the squared deviations by the batch size, 6. But it turns out that dividing by one less than the batch size, that is, by 5 in this case, gives a measure of spread with better statistical properties. (You may have come upon definitions in other places where one is not subtracted in the divisor – and many calculators will calculate the standard deviation in both ways, dividing by either the batch size n or by $n - 1$, so you should check that you know how to make your calculator use the version that divides by $n - 1$ before using it to find a standard deviation in M140.)

The variance

The quantity obtained, for a batch of size n, by calculating the sum of squared deviations and dividing by $n - 1$, is called the **variance** of the batch. It is a measure of spread.

For the programmers, the sum of squared deviations is 147 770, so the variance is

$$\frac{147\,770}{5} = 29\,554.$$

However, this calculation has one drawback. With these data on earnings, the unit of measurement of the original data is £. The batch mean is also in £, so the deviations are measured in £ too. But the *squared* deviations have units of '£²', which look rather strange and are not the original units of measurement of the data. So the final stage in calculating the standard deviation is to take the square root of the variance. That changes the units of measurement back to £. In our example, then, for the programmers the standard deviation is $\sqrt{29\,554} = 171.912\,77$. As with the mean, we shall generally round the standard deviation to one decimal place more than the original data, so in this case to £171.9.

We shall generally denote the standard deviation of a batch of data by the letter s. The steps to calculate its value for a batch of data are summarised in the following box. (This is called 'Method 1' because there is also a 'Method 2' that you will meet later in this subsection.)

> **Calculating the standard deviation: Method 1**
>
> 1. Calculate the mean $\bar{x} = \dfrac{\text{sum}}{\text{size}} = \dfrac{\sum x}{n}$.
> 2. Calculate the deviations $(x - \bar{x})$.
> 3. Square the deviations to give $(x - \bar{x})^2$.
> 4. Calculate the variance by summing the squared deviations, to give $\sum(x - \bar{x})^2$, and dividing by $(n - 1)$: that is,
>
> $$\text{variance } (s^2) = \frac{\sum(x - \bar{x})^2}{n - 1}.$$
>
> 5. Calculate the standard deviation as $s = \sqrt{\text{variance}}$.

Check that you can do these calculations by finding the standard deviation of the earnings for Gradgrind's other workers in the following activity.

Activity 16   *Calculating a standard deviation using Method 1*

Table 15 shows the data values for the other workers, as given originally in Table 13. The first two columns are completed. Calculate the values for the third and fourth columns, and the sum of the fourth column. Then calculate the variance and standard deviation for this batch.

Table 15   Sum of squared deviations

Data x	Mean $\overline{x}$	Deviation $(x - \overline{x})$	Squared deviation $(x - \overline{x})^2$
346	656		
376	656		
391	656		
391	656		
415	656		
465	656		
830	656		
843	656		
876	656		
1627	656		
$\sum$		0	

You may well be thinking that it is quite a tedious business to calculate a standard deviation, using the kind of methods that have been described, using a calculator – and so far the biggest batch you have looked at had only 10 values in it. In practice you will not be expected to do this kind of calculation too often. In M140, and indeed in the real world, standard deviations would typically be calculated in a computer program (Minitab for M140), or perhaps (for small batches) using some special features on a calculator.

If your calculator has features that allow easier calculation of standard deviations, you should use them where appropriate. However, because different calculators deal with this sort of thing differently, it is important that you check how to do so on your own calculator. Also, as previously mentioned, many calculators give you the choice between dividing by n and dividing by $n - 1$ in calculating the variance, and you must therefore be sure to use the $n - 1$ version for M140.

However, there is an alternative method of calculating standard deviations that can be useful on calculators. This second method is illustrated again using the data for Gradgrind's programmers.

The difference between Method 1 (the method you have used so far) and Method 2 (the new method) lies in how the quantity $\sum(x - \overline{x})^2$ is calculated. Up to now, $\sum(x - \overline{x})^2$ has been found by first finding the deviations by subtracting the mean from each data value, then squaring the deviations, and then adding them up. But it turns out that

$$\sum(x - \overline{x})^2 = \sum x^2 - \frac{(\sum x)^2}{n}.$$

This can be proved mathematically, but we shall not do that here as you do not need the proof for M140. We shall just illustrate that it works for the Gradgrind programmers' earnings.

Table 16 shows again, in the first column, the data values for the programmers from Table 13. The second column contains the squares of the data values – not the squares of the deviations (i.e. the squared deviations) that you saw before, but the squares of the original data values. (So, for example, the first value in the second column is $465^2 = 216\,225$.) At the bottom of the table, the sums of both columns are given.

Table 16   Squared data for programmers

Data x	Squared data x^2
465	216 225
484	234 256
620	384 400
654	427 716
855	731 025
858	736 164
$\sum$ 3936	2 729 786

Method 2 requires us to calculate $\sum(x - \overline{x})^2$ as $\sum x^2 - \dfrac{(\sum x)^2}{n}$. Now, $\sum x^2$ is the sum of the second column in Table 16, the sum of the squared data values, 2 729 786. Note that $\sum x^2 = \sum(x^2) = (\sum x^2)$. However, the quantity $(\sum x)^2$ is *not* the same as $\sum x^2$. It is the square of the sum of the data values (not the sum of the squares) and is found by adding the values in the first column and then squaring their sum. That is, $(\sum x)^2 = (3936)^2$. Therefore,

$$\sum(x - \overline{x})^2 = \sum x^2 - \frac{(\sum x)^2}{n}$$
$$= 2\,729\,786 - \frac{3936^2}{6}$$
$$= 2\,729\,786 - \frac{15\,492\,096}{6}$$
$$= 2\,729\,786 - 2\,582\,016 = 147\,770.$$

This result is exactly what you found, using Method 1, for the sum of the squared deviations, $\sum(x - \overline{x})^2$, in Activity 15. The rest of this calculation of the standard deviation follows exactly as it did in Method 1. The variance is

$$\frac{\sum(x - \overline{x})^2}{n - 1} = \frac{147\,770}{5} = 29\,554.$$

The standard deviation is

$$s = \sqrt{\text{variance}} = \sqrt{29\,554} = 171.9 \text{ (to one decimal place)}.$$

You have now covered the material related to Screencast 5 for Unit 3 (see the M140 website).

The steps for calculating the standard deviation of a batch of data by Method 2 are as shown in the following box.

Calculating the standard deviation: Method 2

1.   Calculate the sum of the data values, $\sum x$.

2.   Calculate the sum of the squares of the data values, $\sum x^2$.

3.   Calculate the sum of the squares of the deviations, $\sum (x - \overline{x})^2$, as

$$\sum x^2 - \frac{(\sum x)^2}{n}.$$

4.   Calculate the variance by dividing $\sum (x - \overline{x})^2$ by $(n - 1)$: that is,

$$\text{variance } (s^2) = \frac{\sum (x - \overline{x})^2}{n - 1}.$$

5.   Calculate the standard deviation as $s = \sqrt{\text{variance}}$.

So there are two methods of calculating the standard deviation. Both methods give the same answer, although if you are using a basic calculator it is generally easier to use Method 2. The methods have already been described, but a briefer way to describe them is in the following box.

Sum of squared deviations

- Method 1: Calculate the mean $\overline{x}$, subtract it from each data value and hence work out $\sum (x - \overline{x})^2$ directly.

- Method 2: Calculate the sum of the data values, $\sum x$, and the sum of the squares of the data values, $\sum x^2$, and hence work out
$$\sum (x - \overline{x})^2 = \sum x^2 - \frac{(\sum x)^2}{n}.$$

Then, by either method,

Variance: $s^2 = \dfrac{\sum (x - \overline{x})^2}{n - 1},$

Standard deviation: $s = \sqrt{\text{variance}}.$

'It's the new keyboard for the statistics lab. Once you learn how to use it, it will make computation of the standard deviation easier.'

Activity 17   *Calculating a standard deviation using Method 2*

Using Method 2, calculate the standard deviation for Gradgrind's ten other staff using the data in the first column of Table 17.

Table 17   Squared data for 'other staff'

Data x	Squared data x^2
346	
376	
391	
391	
415	
465	
830	
843	
876	
1627	
Σ	

Start by completing the second column of the table with the squares of the data values and calculating the column sums.

Then calculate the sum of the squared deviations using

$$\sum (x - \overline{x})^2 = \sum x^2 - \frac{(\sum x)^2}{n}.$$

Finally, calculate the variance and standard deviation. (You should, of course, get the same variance and standard deviation as in Activity 16.)

To summarise our findings on spread for the two batches in Table 13, the interquartile ranges (IQR) and the standard deviations (s) are given below.

	Programmers	Other staff
IQR	377	464
s	171.9	403.6

Both measures of spread show that the data for the other staff is more widely spread out than the data for the programmers. But the difference looks much greater in terms of s, where the standard deviation for the other staff is considerably more than twice as large as that for the programmers. The reason is essentially that the batch of earnings for the other staff contains one figure, £1627, that is considerably bigger than all the others in that batch. Just as the mean is not a resistant measure and can be strongly affected by one or two values near the extremes, the standard deviation is also not a resistant measure of spread. The interquartile range, on the other hand, *is* a resistant measure of spread. (This difference between the two measures will be mentioned in Subsection 3.3.)

These ideas were introduced in Subsection 1.4 of Unit 2.

Activity 18 *Standard deviation for all employees*

Using Method 2, calculate the mean and the standard deviation of the combined batch consisting of the earnings of all the employees of Gradgrind Ltd in Table 13. (Hint: you can work out the necessary sums without having to start from scratch, by using the calculations in Table 16 and in the solution to Activity 17.)

You have now covered the material needed for Subsection 3.1 of the Computer Book.

3.2 Calculating the mean and standard deviation for grouped data

Suppose we sampled a large number of families and noted the number of children in each. We could record this information as: 'The first family had two children, the second family had none, the third family had ...'. However, for a large sample the list would be long. It would be easier to group the families together according to the number of children and just record the number of families that had no children, the number with one child, the number with two children, and so on. If no family had more than 15 children then this list would have 16 or fewer items (0 to 15 children). Data recorded in this form are called **grouped data**.

When a batch contains a large number of items, calculating the batch mean and standard deviation might seem a daunting task. With grouped data, however, the amount of labour that is involved depends on the number of groups, and not on the number of individual items. This will be

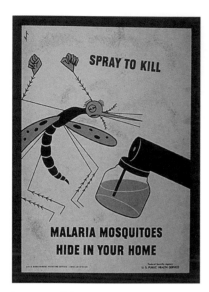

Figure 21 A U.S. government poster from the 1940s aimed at combatting malaria

illustrated using the following data, consisting of 50 000 individual items but only five groups.

The data in Table 18 come from a study of the way in which the malaria parasite *Plasmodium falciparum* invades red blood cells. A sample of blood was taken from a patient with malaria caused by this species of parasite, and the number of parasites in each of 50 000 red blood cells in the sample was counted.

Table 18   Malaria parasites in red blood cells

Number of parasites per cell x	Frequency f
0	40 000
1	8 621
2	1 259
3	99
4	21

(Source: Wang, C.C. (1970) 'Multiple invasion of erythrocyte by malaria parasites', *Transactions of the Royal Society of Tropical Medicine and Hygiene*, vol. 64, issue 2, pp. 268–270)

The data presented in Table 18 is an example of grouped data. Each row of the table corresponds to a different group. The numbers in the table mean that there were (exactly!) 40 000 cells that contained no parasites at all, 8621 with exactly one parasite, 1259 with two parasites, and so on. No cell contained more than four parasites.

> The term **frequencies** is used for numbers (such as those in the second column of Table 18) which tell us how frequent the corresponding data values are. We shall generally denote frequencies by f.

How do we calculate the mean and standard deviation of the grouped data in Table 18? It turns out that we need the batch size, the sum of the values and the sum of their squares. The following example shows how these can be obtained.

Example 5   *Malaria parasites: calculations with grouped data*

Obtaining the batch size for the grouped data in Table 18 is easy. There are 40 000 blood cells that had no parasites, 8621 had one, 1259 had two, 99 had three, and 21 had four, so we obtain the batch size by adding the numbers in the frequency column. That is, the batch size equals the total number of blood cells:

$$\sum f = 40\,000 + 8621 + 1259 + 99 + 21 = 50\,000.$$

Now, for the sum of the data values, imagine that for all of the 50 000 cells we decided to write out in a row the number of parasites in each cell and add them up. In this sum, there would be 40 000 zeros, which contribute $0 \times 40\,000$, that is, zero, to the sum; 8621 ones, which contribute $1 \times 8621 = 8621$ to the sum; 1259 twos which contribute $2 \times 1259 = 2518$ to the sum, and so on. That is, to get the sum of the data values, we calculate, for each row of the table, the product xf, and then we sum these products. This is shown in Table 19.

Table 19 Malaria parasites: calculating the sum

x	f	xf
0	40 000	0
1	8 621	8 621
2	1 259	2 518
3	99	297
4	21	84
$\sum$	50 000	11 520

That is, the total number of parasites in the whole batch of blood cells can be obtained by summing the number of parasites in each group:

$$\sum xf = 0 + 8621 + 2518 + 297 + 84 = 11520.$$

The sum of the squares of the data values can be calculated in a similar way. The 40 000 zeros each contribute $0^2 = 0$ to the sum, so their total contribution to the sum of squares is 0. The 8621 ones each contribute $1^2 = 1$, so their total contribution to the sum of squares is $8621 \times 1^2 = 8621$. The 1259 twos each contribute $2^2 = 4$, so their total contribution to the sum of squares is $1259 \times 4 = 5036$. And so on. That is, we get the sum of squares by multiplying x^2, the *square* of each data value, by the corresponding frequency, f, and summing the resulting quantities – that is, we calculate $\sum x^2 f$. These calculations are shown in Table 20.

Table 20 Malaria parasites: calculating the sum of the squares

x	x^2	f	xf	$x^2 f$
0	0	40 000	0	0
1	1	8621	8621	8621
2	4	1259	2518	5036
3	9	99	297	891
4	16	21	84	336
		$\sum f = 50\,000$	$\sum xf = 11\,520$	$\sum x^2 f = 14\,884$

So, the sum of the squares of the data values is

$$\sum x^2 f = 14\,884.$$

Now we have calculated the batch size, the sum of the values and the sum of their squares, we can calculate the mean and standard deviation for the grouped data using the following method. It is the same as Method 2 for ungrouped data, but with n, $\sum x$ and $\sum x^2$ replaced with $\sum f$, $\sum xf$ and $\sum x^2 f$.

Mean and standard deviation from grouped data

Denoting the data values by x and the corresponding frequencies by f:

1. Construct a table similar to Table 20 to calculate the batch size, $n = \sum f$, the sum of the data values, $\sum xf$, and the sum of the squares of the data values, $\sum x^2 f$.

2. Calculate the mean as $\bar{x} = \dfrac{\sum xf}{n}$.

3. Calculate the sum of the squares of the deviations as
$$\sum (x - \bar{x})^2 f = \sum x^2 f - \frac{(\sum xf)^2}{n}.$$

4. Divide the result of step 3 by $n - 1$, giving
$$\text{variance } (s^2) = \frac{\sum (x - \bar{x})^2 f}{n - 1}.$$

5. Calculate the standard deviation as $s = \sqrt{\text{variance}}$.

Example 6 *Malaria parasites: calculating the mean*

Using the totals in Table 20, the batch size of the malaria parasite data is
$$n = \sum f = 50\,000$$
and the sum of the data values is
$$\sum xf = 11\,520.$$

So we can calculate the mean as:
$$\bar{x} = \frac{\text{total number of parasites}}{\text{total number of blood cells}} = \frac{\sum xf}{\sum f}$$
$$= \frac{11\,520}{50\,000} = 0.2304 \simeq 0.2.$$

Therefore, on average, there are approximately 0.2 parasites per red blood cell.

Activity 19 *Malaria parasites: calculating the standard deviation*

Using the totals given in Table 20, calculate the standard deviation for the number of parasites in a red blood cell.

Activity 20   *Flying bomb hits*

The (grouped) data in Table 21 come from a study of the sites where flying bombs hit South London during World War Two (see Figure 22). The whole area was divided into 576 squares, each one quarter of a square kilometre, and the number of hits in each square was counted. (The purpose of the study was to investigate whether the flying bombs were precisely aimed, or instead just aimed in the general direction of London where they then landed at random. The conclusion was that the bombs were *not* precisely aimed.)

Calculate the mean number of hits per square, and the standard deviation of the number of hits per square.

Table 21   Flying bomb hits

Number of hits per square x	Frequency f
0	229
1	211
2	93
3	35
4	7
5	1

(Source: Clarke, R.D. (1946) 'An application of the Poisson distribution', *Journal of the Institute of Actuaries*, vol. 72, p. 481)

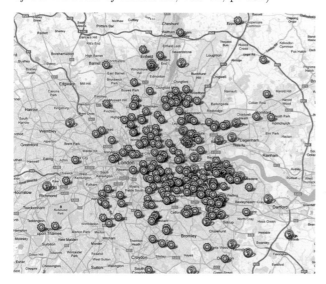

Figure 22   Map of London indicating where flying bombs landed

You have now covered the material related to Screencast 6 for Unit 3 (see the M140 website).

3.3   Deciding which measure to use

You know how to find the two major measures of spread: the standard deviation and the interquartile range. So you may well be wondering how to decide which one to use. This is very similar to deciding whether to use the mean or the median as a measure of location (see Subsection 1.4 of Unit 2). Among the factors to bear in mind are the following.

- *Consistency.* Owing to their similarities, these measures tend to be used in the following pairs:

  - the mean and standard deviation

  - the median and interquartile range.

  It is quite rare to present an analysis which uses the median to measure location and the standard deviation to measure spread, or the mean to measure location and the interquartile range to measure spread. The reason that these measures tend to go together in this way is to do with the underlying arithmetic operations that are used in their calculation. Essentially, the mean and standard deviation involve adding, while the median and interquartile range are based on counting.

- *Purpose.* For the next stage in your analysis of the data, you may require one measure rather than the other. Later in M140 you will meet some methods that use medians, and others that use means and standard deviations. When choosing your measure, you should bear in mind which other methods you are going to use when analysing the data.

A *resistant* measure is one which is not particularly affected by changes in the values near the extremes. (See Subsection 1.4 of Unit 2.)

- *Resistance.* Just as the mean is less resistant than the median, the standard deviation is less resistant than the interquartile range. The greater resistance of the interquartile range was referred to in Subsection 3.1 (just before Activity 18), in the context of the Gradgrind earnings figures. It is explored further in the following activities.

Activity 21   *Resistance of measures of spread*

Suppose that the lowest and highest values in the batch of earnings of Gradgrind's 'other' staff (Table 13 of Subsection 3.1) were altered to 246 and 1727. Find the interquartile range and the standard deviation of the new batch. The *original* data for the other staff is repeated here for convenience.

346   376   391   391   415   465   830   843   876   1627

There are two key points to emerge from the calculations for Activity 21:

- Despite having altered two of the values, the interquartile range remains unchanged from its original value of 464.

- By making the distribution more spread out, the two alterations have increased the standard deviation from its original value of 403.6 to 440.0. (The value of 403.6 for the standard deviation was calculated in Activity 16 of Subsection 3.1.)

In the next section, you will see how to use Minitab to calculate some of the summary measures from this unit and Unit 2, and how to draw boxplots.

Exercises on Section 3

Exercise 6 *Winter energy consumption*

Calculate the mean and standard deviation of each of the two batches of data in Table 22. (MWh is the usual abbreviation for megawatt hours.)

Table 22 Winter energy consumptions (MWh) of ten houses in Bristol before and after insulation

Before insulation	After insulation
12.1	12.0
11.0	10.6
14.1	13.4
13.8	11.2
15.5	15.3
12.2	13.6
12.8	12.6
9.9	8.8
10.8	9.6
12.7	12.4

Exercise 7 *Counting Macaulay's words*

In a study aimed at developing a method of characterising an author's style, samples of ten words were taken from the beginning of each of 100 randomly chosen lines from the printed text of *Macaulay's Essay on Milton* (T.B. Macaulay, 1895). In each ten-word sample, the number of times that the three article words 'the', 'a' and 'an' appeared was counted. The data appear (in grouped form) in Table 23. Calculate the mean and standard deviation for these data.

Table 23 Articles in Macaulay

Number of articles x	Frequency f
0	27
1	44
2	26
3	3

(Source: Bailey, B.J.R. (1990) 'A model for function word counts', *Applied Statistics*, vol. 39, no. 1, pp. 107–114)

4 Computer work: summary measures and boxplots

In Unit 1 you were introduced to the Minitab software. In this section, you will learn how to use Minitab to calculate some of the summary measures you have learned about in Units 2 and 3 – means, medians, quartiles, interquartile range and standard deviations. You will also learn how to draw boxplots with Minitab.

You should now turn to the Computer Book and work through Subsection 3.1, if you have not already done so, followed by the rest of Chapter 3.

5 Prices and earnings

A central question which ran through Unit 2 was: *Are people getting better or worse off?* You saw there that this is a difficult question to answer precisely. For a start, there are many different factors to take into account; also, what may be true for one person will not necessarily be true for another. However, it is clear that two key factors, prices and earnings, are highly relevant to the question. Unit 2 and this unit have been devoted to considering how these two factors can be measured.

In this final section, we shall attempt to bring together prices and earnings to see how they compare over time. We start with earnings and consider a drawback inherent in data taken from the Annual Survey of Hours and Earnings (ASHE).

You know already from Subsection 1.3 that the ASHE does not cover the earnings of self-employed people (or indeed unemployed people). Another major drawback, for some purposes, is that the survey is carried out only once a year. This is far less frequent than the price indices (RPI and CPI) that you met in Unit 2, which are published monthly. In monitoring the economy, data that come out only once a year are not frequent enough for the government. Further data on earnings are available from the Labour Force Survey, which is a major data source for (among other things) measures of unemployment that go beyond simply counting up how many people are claiming out-of-work benefits; it also collects data on earnings from its respondents. (The Labour Force Survey collects its data from individual respondents, not their employers. This leads to some issues of accuracy because, in some cases, the responses are given by a person other than the actual income earner if they are not available for interview, and that person may not know the level of income closely enough.)

The Labour Force Survey publishes earnings data every three months, but even that is not frequent enough for some purposes. We shall therefore turn to an alternative measure of income, published monthly, called the Average Weekly Earnings (AWE) index.

5.1 The Average Weekly Earnings (AWE) index

In this subsection, we are going to look at an index which measures *changes* in most people's main source of income: their earnings. This index is the Average Weekly Earnings (AWE) index, calculated by the ONS once a month. We will describe briefly how the data used for the AWE index are collected and how the index is calculated. Then, at the end of the section, we will describe how the AWE index, together with the CPI can be used to investigate the economic health of society.

The AWE index is based on the Average Weekly Earnings measure. Here are some extracts from the official description of the measure.

> The Average Weekly Earnings (AWE) measure is the Office for National Statistics' (ONS's) lead indicator of short-term changes in earnings. ... AWE is published monthly and is designed to capture changes in average earnings of employees in Great Britain. ... Average Weekly Earnings is calculated from returns to the Monthly Wages and Salaries Survey (MWSS), and is weighted to be representative of the Great Britain economy as a whole. The self-employed, HM Armed Forces and Government Supported Trainees are excluded from the statistics.

> (Source: ONS (2011) *Quality and Methodology Information for Average Weekly Earnings*)

To find out what is meant here by earnings, we must look at the data which are used to calculate the AWE measure. These data come from a survey called the Monthly Wages and Salaries Survey. Each month, a sample of around 9000 firms in Great Britain receives a simple questionnaire whose main purpose is to obtain the following figures.

The survey does not cover Northern Ireland.

- The number of monthly-paid employees receiving pay in that month.

- The total gross amount paid to all monthly-paid employees during that month.

- The number of weekly-paid employees receiving pay during the last pay-week in that month.

- The total gross amount paid to all weekly-paid employees during that week.

Employers are specifically asked to include overtime and holiday pay, as well as other additional payments, in their returns, and not to make deductions for tax, national insurance and pension contributions, etc. They are asked to exclude fees paid to directors, trainees on government schemes, and certain other categories. The questionnaire also asks employers to provide data on arrears of pay, such as those arising from backdated pay increases. These arrears are included in the gross pay amounts, but are subtracted from them when calculating the index based on the AWE measure.

So we now know that, in the Average Weekly Earnings measure, **earnings** simply means *the gross amounts paid to employees (excluding pay arrears)*. Now let us look at how these data are used to calculate an index that measures *changes* in the overall level of earnings.

1. The first step is to find the average weekly earnings for each of the businesses in the sample. For those paid monthly, their pay is converted to a weekly figure. Then the average weekly earnings is calculated by dividing the total gross amount paid to all employees by the number of employees.

2. The next step is to calculate a national figure for average weekly earnings, as a weighted average of the data for each business. The weighting that is used is rather complicated, taking into account the size of the business, the industry it is in, and whether it is public or private, but in principle this is simply a weighted average (that is, a weighted mean) like those you met in Unit 2.

3. Next, the average weekly earning figures are *seasonally adjusted*. This means that they are adjusted to allow for the effect of changes in earnings levels that occur regularly at fixed times of the year. Thus, if the AWE measure shows an increase between one month and the next, this means that wages have gone up (on average) that month by *more* than they would normally be expected to increase at that time of year.

4. Finally, the Average Weekly Earnings index is calculated by comparing the national average weekly earnings with the corresponding figure for the base year. At the time of writing (2012), the base year is 2000 and the AWE index for 2000 is set at 100. Like the CPI (but unlike the RPI), for the AWE index the average earnings are compared with the average over the whole base year, and not just a single month. That is, the value of the AWE index for a given month is

    $$100 \times \frac{\text{average weekly earnings in that month}}{\text{average weekly earnings in the base year}}.$$

    This differs from both the RPI and CPI, in that the comparison is made *directly* with base date. With the AWE index, there is no chaining.

The Average Weekly Earnings index thus provides information on changes in the overall level of earnings in Great Britain. Figures for the index, together with the average weekly earnings on which it is based, are published each month on the ONS website. Although versions of the index are published for different sectors of the economy, we shall only use the index for the whole economy.

You have now learnt about two sources of earnings data: the AWE index and the ASHE. The most important difference (apart from their frequency) is that, whilst ASHE measures the *level* of earnings of different groups, the AWE index is primarily designed to measure *changes* in earnings. (Data on average earnings levels *are* published for AWE, but its design is primarily aimed at looking at changes.) Another difference is that, whereas ASHE covers a sample of *individuals*, the AWE index covers a sample of *firms*. A simple way of comparing the two sources would be to say that the AWE index uses a quick, relatively cheap survey which is designed for a specific purpose (looking at overall changes in earnings levels), whereas ASHE is a more detailed, general-purpose survey.

No doubt you will have noticed a considerable degree of similarity between the calculation of the AWE index and that of the RPI and CPI described in Unit 2. We are now ready to put together the AWE index and one of the price measures, the CPI, and compare price and income changes over the period from 2001 to 2011.

5.2 Comparing the AWE with the CPI

> 'Annual income twenty pounds, annual expenditure nineteen nineteen and six, result happiness. Annual income twenty pounds, annual expenditure twenty pounds ought and six, result misery.'

> (Source: Mr Micawber in Charles Dickens' *David Copperfield* (1850))

Our motivation for investigating the AWE index is to use it in conjunction with a *price* index to measure the economic well-being of the nation. For this purpose we shall use the CPI rather than the RPI.

The balance between pay and prices is often a precarious one and Mr Micawber's comment (quoted above) is particularly pertinent when pay and prices are rising rapidly, for it is then often difficult to ensure that both rise in step. A statistical Mr Micawber might well say: 'AWE index exceeds CPI, result happiness. CPI exceeds AWE index, result misery'. Because the CPI measures only price changes, to make such a comparison we must compare changes in both the indices over a given period. In Unit 2 you learned how to express changes in the RPI and CPI. We shall now see how to do the same thing with the AWE index.

Figure 23   An image of Mr Micawber

Example 7 *Calculating a change in the AWE index*

The value of the AWE index for January 2011 was 144.7 and the value for January 2012 was 145.4. Therefore its value in January 2012 as a percentage of its January 2011 value was

$$\frac{145.4}{144.7} \times 100\% = 100.483\,76\% \simeq 100.5\%.$$

Thus its increase over the year January 2011 to January 2012 was 0.5% of its January 2011 value. That is, earnings on average did increase over that year, but only by half of one per cent.

Figure 24 Another CPI. Does it fill you with AWE?

Activity 22 *Percentage change in the AWE index*

The value of the AWE index for January 2000 was 98.2 and the value for January 2001 was 103.6. By what percentage of the January 2000 value did the AWE index increase over the year?

To compare changes in the CPI with those in the AWE index we need to calculate the changes in both indices. This is shown in Figure 25, covering the period from 2001 to 2011. The graph reveals that, during the middle years of the decade, the increase in the AWE index remained fairly steady at around 4% per annum and was at a level consistently higher than the average price rises (shown by the CPI). After the beginning of 2008, though, earnings increases fell below the level of price increases, and generally remained so right up to the end of the period covered. (The extreme negative values of the change in the AWE index in early 2009, and the high positive values in early 2010 and 2011, are due to large fluctuations in bonus pay, particularly in the financial sector.)

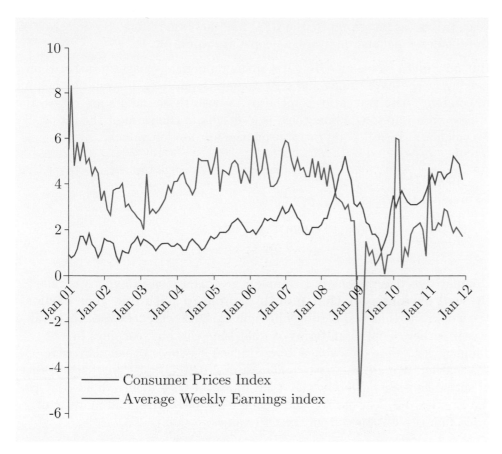

Figure 25 Changes in the CPI and the AWE index, 2001–2011 (percentage increases over previous year)

(Data source: Office for National Statistics)

On the basis of these data, for people in the UK from 2009 to 2011 the 'average' answer to the question *Are people getting better or worse off?* is pretty clearly *Worse off!*.

The overall point here is essentially Mr Micawber's point. If, over the last year, your pay has gone up by more than prices went up, you can now buy everything you could buy a year ago, and more, and you are better off. If instead your pay has gone up by less than prices went up, you can no longer buy everything you could buy a year ago and you are worse off.

Example 8 *Comparing the changes in two indices*

The values of the CPI in January 2011 and January 2012 were 116.9 and 121.1 respectively. Thus its value in January 2012 as a percentage of its value one year earlier was

$$\frac{121.1}{116.9} \times 100\% = 103.592\,81\% \simeq 103.6\%.$$

We can now compare the changes in the two indices, calculated here and in Example 7. The AWE index in January 2012 was 100.5% of its value one year earlier. Thus earnings had increased (slightly), but over the same year, prices (as measured by the CPI) had increased more. So, in terms of these index numbers, on average people are worse off.

But *how much* worse off? To get a single numerical measure, rather than looking at the AWE index and CPI changes separately, it would be helpful to combine these two ratios somehow. As both these indices are ratios, the appropriate way to combine them is to calculate the ratio of the ratios. So we calculate the following ratio (using the unrounded values):

$$\frac{100.483\,76}{103.592\,81}.$$

Expressing the answer as a percentage:

$$\frac{100.483\,76}{103.592\,81} \times 100\% = 96.998\,78\% \simeq 97.0\%.$$

Comparisons like the one in Example 8 give us a measure which is called the **real earnings for that month compared with one year earlier**. We would say that real earnings in January 2012 were 97.0% of their value a year earlier. That is, in terms of what they can buy, earnings in January 2012 were on average lower (indeed 3% lower) than they were one year earlier. We use the term 'real earnings' here because we take the ratio of actual earnings, given by the AWE index for that month divided by the AWE index one year earlier, and divide it by the corresponding ratio of price changes, obtained from the CPI values.

To calculate this measure directly, it can help to do a bit of rearranging. In Example 8, the ratio for comparing the CPI values over the year was

$$\frac{\text{CPI for January 2012}}{\text{CPI for one year earlier}}.$$

The corresponding ratio for comparing the AWE index values, from Example 7, was

$$\frac{\text{AWE index for January 2012}}{\text{AWE index for one year earlier}}.$$

Then, to get the real earnings measure, we divided the ratio calculated from the AWE index values by the corresponding ratio for the CPI, to give

$$\frac{\text{AWE index for January 2012}}{\text{AWE index for one year earlier}} \bigg/ \frac{\text{CPI for January 2012}}{\text{CPI for one year earlier}},$$

which can be rearranged (using the usual rules for arithmetic with fractions) to

$$\frac{\text{AWE index for January 2012}}{\text{AWE index for one year earlier}} \times \frac{\text{CPI for one year earlier}}{\text{CPI for January 2012}}.$$

So, in general, we use the following formula.

Real earnings for month A compared with one year earlier

The real earnings for month A compared with one year earlier is defined as:
$$\frac{\text{AWE index for month A}}{\text{AWE index for one year earlier}} \times \frac{\text{CPI for one year earlier}}{\text{CPI for month A}}.$$

To illustrate this calculation we shall use the list of the values of both the CPI and the AWE index in Table 24.

Table 24   Values of the CPI and AWE index in 2010 and 2011

	CPI 2010	CPI 2011	AWE index 2010	AWE index 2011
January	112.4	116.9	138.1	144.7
February	112.9	117.8	141.2	144.0
March	113.5	118.1	142.8	145.7
April	114.2	119.3	141.2	144.4
May	114.4	119.5	111.7	144.8
June	114.6	119.4	141.3	145.4
July	114.3	119.4	141.8	145.9
August	114.9	120.1	142.5	145.7
September	114.9	120.9	143.1	145.8
October	115.2	121.0	143.3	146.4
November	115.6	121.2	143.3	146.0
December	116.8	121.7	143.4	145.8

Example 9   *Annual change in real earnings*

The real earnings for December 2011 compared with one year earlier is:
$$\frac{\text{AWE index for December 2011}}{\text{AWE index for December 2010}} \times \frac{\text{CPI for December 2010}}{\text{CPI for December 2011}}$$
$$= \frac{145.8}{143.4} \times \frac{116.8}{121.7}$$
$$= 0.9757996 \simeq 0.976 = 97.6\%.$$

So the real earnings for December 2011 were 97.6% of their value a year earlier.

Activity 23   *Annual changes at three time points*

For each of the following months calculate, as a percentage, the real earnings for that month compared with one year earlier. (Round your answers to one decimal place.)

(a) March 2011   (b) June 2011   (c) September 2011

The calculation from Activity 23 has been done for every month in 2011, with Table 25 (below) showing the results (rounded to one decimal place).

Table 25   Real earnings in 2011 compared with one year earlier

	Jan	Feb	March	April	May	June	July	Aug	Sept	Oct	Nov	Dec
%	100.7	97.7	98.1	97.9	97.8	98.8	98.5	97.8	96.8	97.3	97.2	97.6

There appears to be no obvious trend in these figures. The January figure shows a small increase in real earnings compared to the previous year (which was due largely to an increase in annual bonuses compared to the year before). Apart from that, every month shows a decrease in real earnings compared to the previous year.

5.3   Points to consider when using the AWE

The AWE index, like all statistics, can be misused. It cannot provide information for which it was not designed and so it must be used with care and common sense.

To conclude this section and the unit, you are asked to consider four points and to think how they could influence the use of the AWE index.

Averages are not individuals

The AWE index, like the CPI and RPI, is based on *averages* and should *not* be taken as representing the circumstances of any *particular individual* or individuals. So the AWE index and the CPI, even when used together, provide only a very poor assessment of whether a *particular group* of people is getting better or worse off.

Average means mean

In Subsection 5.1, the word *average* in the AWE index is always interpreted as *mean* or *weighted mean*. These both depend on the sum of the values in a particular batch. Remember that the formula is

$$\text{mean} = \frac{\text{sum}}{\text{size}}.$$

If the sum and the size remain the same, then the mean is unchanged, no matter how the individual values vary within the batch.

For example, suppose that Pat Gradgrind, the managing director of Gradgrind Ltd, receives a pay *increase* of £10 000 per year, and that each of ten cleaners in the firm gets a *decrease* of £1000 per year. Think for a few moments what effect this might have on the AWE index.

Changes such as that above will not affect the value of the AWE index even if Gradgrind is included in the Monthly Wages and Salaries Survey on which the AWE index is based. This is because the *total* amount paid (the sum) has not been changed, nor has the number of employees (the size). In short, the AWE index is not sensitive to such changes in the overall distribution of earnings – it is concerned only with *averages* (which, here, means means).

The AWE index and unemployment

A further problem connected with the AWE index can also be illustrated by events at Gradgrind Ltd. Suppose now that, instead of losing some earnings, the cleaners are all made redundant. What do you think the effect of this on the AWE index would be? (Not to mention the effect on the cleanliness of Gradgrind's premises!)

Cleaners are likely to be among the lowest-paid workers at Gradgrind, so if the cleaners are laid off, then the average pay of those remaining will go up. This means that the AWE index will increase! This may seem paradoxical, and is indeed difficult to understand given the feeling that if the AWE index is *increasing* then people are *getting better off*.

However, the paradox is resolved when we realise that the AWE index is based *only on those in employment* so it can increase purely as a result of lower-paid workers being laid off.

The impact of income tax

In the UK, income tax is charged on all income over a certain amount each year. For example, suppose that a typical UK taxpayer paid no income tax on the first £8000 of earnings but paid tax at the rate of 20% on all income above this. (We shall use these numbers here just to illustrate the points we are making. In practice, in the UK the *actual* numbers change every year, or thereabouts, with the changes generally being announced in the Budget statement.)

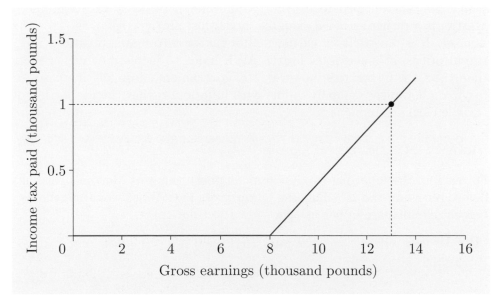

Figure 26 Relationship between income tax and gross earnings

This link between earnings and tax payable is shown in Figure 26. For example, an individual earning £13 000 each year pays tax on the earnings above £8000. This means a 20% charge on £5000 – that is, a tax bill of £1000 for that year.

Has this anything to do with the AWE index? Yes, it has, because it affects how much *earnings* must increase to compensate for a given increase in *prices*.

Suppose further that, as measured by the CPI, *prices* increase by 10%, and that the AWE index also increases by 10%. On the surface, it would appear that, on average, people would be just as well off as before – however, that is not the case.

To illustrate the problem, consider Martha Greenslade, one of the cleaners at Gradgrind Ltd, who earns exactly £8000 per year. Martha therefore pays no tax. Now suppose that Martha is an 'average' person in the sense that she gets a pay increase equal to the increase in the AWE index, namely 10%. In other words, Martha's earnings increase from £8000 to £8800 per year.

However, these are *gross* earnings. Martha has now gone into the 20% tax bracket, so she must pay this rate of tax on the whole of her increase. Therefore the increase in her *net* earnings is not £800, but only £640. (*Net income* is gross income minus the amount of tax paid.) In other words, an increase of 10% in her *gross* earnings has been transformed by taxation into an increase of only 8% in her *net* earnings. If the CPI went up by 10% and if Martha wanted to match this by a 10% increase in her *net* earnings (after all, it is her *net* earnings out of which she must pay the higher prices) then the increase in her *gross* earnings would have to be 12.5%, since this is the increase which reduces to 10% after allowing for taxation.

Of course, different people are affected in different ways by taxation, and Martha is a rather artificial example, being just on the edge of the 20% tax bracket. It is true that for earnings after taxation to match inflation (the rise in prices) it is necessary for the AWE index to increase by rather more than the CPI. In practice, however, UK governments normally increase tax-free allowances annually in line with inflation so that the proportion of taxable earnings remains roughly the same.

Activity 24   *Changes in Martha's net pay*

For each of the following two amounts, suppose this was Martha's earnings before receiving the 10% increase in her gross pay. What would be the percentage increase in her net pay?

(a) £7500

(b) £8500

A clear message of Subsection 5.3 has been that making judgements about people's earnings based solely on averages like the AWE index can be very misleading. Indeed, the same warnings need to be applied to all available average measures of earnings and price changes – they draw only on data taken from an incomplete population and they say nothing about the inequalities experienced by individuals. Taken overall, the increases of average earnings did seem to have exceeded price rises from 2001 to about the end of 2007, although from then until the time of writing (2012) at least, the position is reversed and price rises have generally been exceeding rises in average earnings. So, are people getting better or worse off? In an important sense it depends on the timescale. Since 2008 up to the time of writing, on average people are *not* getting better off. But, for instance, AWE index and CPI figures can be used to calculate the real earnings in January 2012 as a percentage of the real earnings in January 2000. In terms of that measure, real earnings increased by 12.6% over that twelve-year period (even though it includes the period since 2008 during which real earnings were decreasing). However, earnings inequalities have widened since 2000 (and indeed for some time before that). So, compared to the position of the highest earners, the position of those on low pay has got worse. We have some partial answers to the question *Are people getting better or worse off?*, but in some ways the main thing that we have learned is that this question has no straightforward answer.

Summary

In this unit you have learned how statistics can answer questions connected with people's earnings. You have learned how to calculate earnings ratios at different points across distributions. These ratios summarise the pay differential between men's and women's earnings. They can depend on factors such as the inclusion or exclusion of overtime, the numbers of hours worked, the sector (public or private) and the occupation.

You have learned more about boxplots, including how to recognise skewness in a data from a boxplot and how to construct boxplots, both by hand and by using Minitab. In ordinary boxplots, the ends of the whiskers represent the upper and lower adjacent values, whereas, in decile boxplots, the ends of the whiskers represent the highest and lowest deciles.

A new measure of spread – the standard deviation – has been described. The standard deviation is paired with the mean, whereas the interquartile range is paired with the median. You learned two methods to calculate the standard deviation by hand, along with how to obtain the standard deviation and other summary measures, using Minitab. You also learned how to calculate the mean and standard deviation by hand for grouped data.

The Average Weekly Earnings index is published by the Office for National Statistics and measures the changes in earnings. By comparing this index with the CPI, you have been able to calculate real earnings compared with a year before and hence go some way to answering the question: *Are people getting better or worse off?*

Finally, you have been introduced to some surveys which collect data on earnings in the UK. You have seen how the way the data are collected can limit the conclusions which can be drawn from an analysis.

Learning outcomes

After working through this unit, you should be able to:

- calculate earnings ratios and understand how they measure the discrepancy between men's and women's earnings
- describe briefly the Annual Survey of Hours and Earnings (ASHE) and some of the data which it collects
- use the median, quartiles, and highest and lowest deciles to describe large batches of data
- interpret decile boxplots
- understand that, in order to compare like with like, it is essential to select from published sources of data with great care
- interpret and compare boxplots in terms of skewness
- draw a boxplot, dealing appropriately with adjacent values and potential outliers
- calculate the standard deviation of a batch of data
- calculate the mean and standard deviation for a batch of grouped data
- understand some of the factors affecting the choice of summary measures for a batch of data
- use Minitab to do further numerical calculations on data
- use Minitab to obtain and customise boxplots
- describe what is meant in the Average Weekly Earnings (AWE) by earnings
- describe the main stages involved in the calculation of the AWE index
- compare changes in the AWE index with changes in the CPI
- calculate real earnings compared with a year earlier
- describe how the interpretation of the AWE index is affected by:
  - the distribution of earnings
  - unemployment
  - taxation.

Solutions to activities

Solution to Activity 1

(a) Women worked 37.4 hours per week on average. This is fewer hours than the average worked by men, which was 40.2 hours.

(b) On average, men did 1.0 hours more overtime per week than women $(1.5 - 0.5 = 1.0)$. Alternatively, men did three times as much overtime as women $(1.5/0.5 = 3)$.

(c) Removing overtime pay from the gross weekly earnings figures would reduce the men's figure more than the women's figure, since men did more overtime. You would expect this to narrow the 'gap' between men's earnings and women's earnings and therefore *increase* the earnings ratio.

(d) Since men worked more hours per week on average than women, you would expect men's gross weekly earnings to be more than women's, even if they were paid the same for similar amounts of work. A fairer comparison might be to look at the gross *hourly* earnings of men and women. This would eliminate the effect on earnings of men working more hours per week than women.

Solution to Activity 2

(a) The earnings ratio at the mean based on weekly earnings excluding overtime is

$$\frac{509}{635} \simeq 0.801\,57 \text{ or } 80\%.$$

(b) The earnings ratio at the mean based on hourly earnings is

$$\frac{1382}{1643} \simeq 0.841\,14 \text{ or } 84\%.$$

(c) Removing overtime pay from gross weekly earnings increases the earnings ratio at the mean from 78% to 80%. Comparing hourly earnings instead of weekly earnings increases the earnings ratio at the mean further to 84%.

Solution to Activity 3

(a) The earnings ratio at the median for gross weekly earnings including overtime is calculated as

$$\frac{440}{538} \simeq 0.817\,84,$$

or 82% after rounding to the nearest one per cent.

The other earnings ratios at the median are calculated similarly, and all of them are given in the table below.

Earnings ratios at the median	%
Gross weekly earnings including overtime	82
Gross weekly earnings excluding overtime	85
Gross hourly earnings excluding overtime	90

(b) As was the case when using the mean, the earnings ratio at the median increases when overtime is excluded and again when hourly earnings are considered instead of weekly earnings. In each case, the earnings ratio at the median is higher than the corresponding earnings ratio at the mean.

Solution to Activity 4

(a) As, by definition, 50% of people earn less than the median wage, a person of median earnings will pass by halfway through the parade at 10:30 am.

(b) You were told that a person of mean height passes by 25 minutes before the end of the parade – that is, at 10:35 am. This is later than the time a person of median earning passes, and reflects the fact that the mean earnings is greater than the median earnings – as is generally the case for right-skew data like these.

Because 10:35 am is 35/60 of the way through the hour, 35/60 or 58% of people earn less than the mean wage. (Actually, the proportion is over 60% as the precise time that a person of average height would pass is actually about 23 minutes before the end, not 25.)

Solution to Activity 5

See text below the activity for discussion of this.

Solution to Activity 6

(a) The 25th percentile has 25%, that is, one quarter, of the batch below it. The 75th percentile has three-quarters of the batch below it, so one quarter of the batch above it. Therefore these two percentiles are actually the quartiles. The 25th percentile is the lower quartile, and the 75th percentile is the upper quartile.

(b) The 50th percentile has 50%, that is, half, the batch below it, and therefore half the batch above it. Thus it is the median, so from the table the 50th percentile is £432 for women and £509 for men.

Solution to Activity 7

(a) 1083 is the highest decile for the group, so 10% of the men earned more than £1083.

(b) 284 and 509 are, respectively, the lowest decile and the median, so 40% of these men earned between £284 and £509.

(c) 364 is the lower quartile, so 25% of the 10 652 000 men, or about 2 663 000 men, earned less than £364.

Solution to Activity 8

The earnings ratios for the upper quartile is

$$\frac{619}{738} = 0.838\,753,$$

which is 84% to the nearest one per cent. The other earnings ratios, calculated similarly, are 87% at the lower quartile, 76% at the highest decile and 89% at the lowest decile. (Rounded from 86.8132%, 75.7156% and 89.0845%.)

Solution to Activity 9

(a) The following table shows the earnings ratio at the median for each year.

Year	1997	1998	1999	2000	2001	2002	2003	2004
Earnings ratio (%)	83	83	84	84	84	85	85	85

Year	2005	2006	2007	2008	2009	2010	2011
Earnings ratio (%)	87	87	88	87	88	90	90

(b) There was a slow, steady increase in the earnings ratio over this period.

(c) Since the earnings ratio has increased, this measure suggests gender inequalities in earnings have narrowed.

Solution to Activity 10

Here are the earnings ratios (in percentages) for each group. The all-workers earnings ratios are also given again, so as to make comparisons easier.

	Public	Private	All
Highest decile	79	72	76
Upper quartile	86	77	84
Median	87	78	85
Lower quartile	88	81	87
Lowest decile	90	86	89

The earnings ratios for public sector workers are higher than those for all workers, and the ratios for private sector workers are noticeably lower than those for all workers. Therefore, women's earnings seem to be nearer to men's earnings in the public sector than in the private sector, with the earnings ratios calculated across all workers being somewhere in between.

However, the earnings ratios for all workers together are closer to those for the public sector than those for the private sector, throughout the range, but particularly towards the lower end.

Solution to Activity 11

The earnings ratios shown below suggest that there are clear differences between occupations. For example, women who are managers and directors in retail and wholesale seem particularly underpaid, especially at the middle and top of the earnings scale, whereas in secondary education, the gender gap is relatively narrow, and it is almost (but not quite!) non-existent for kitchen and catering assistants.

Occupation	Sales and retail assistants			Secondary education professionals			Kitchen and catering assistants			Managers and directors in retail/wholesale		
	M	W	R	M	W	R	M	W	R	M	W	R
Upper quartile	352	312	89	852	801	94	297	283	95	698	497	71
Median	289	260	90	737	699	95	247	245	99	502	374	75
Lower quartile	248	227	92	624	560	90	216	213	99	383	302	79

M: Men   W: Women   R: Earnings ratio

Solution to Activity 12

(a) The boxplot for the arithmetic scores is shown below. Here the left whisker of the boxplot is much longer than the right. Also, the left part of the box is much longer than the right part. Both of these characteristics indicate that this batch is left-skew.

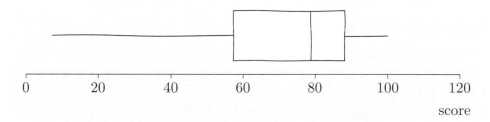

(b) The boxplot for the coffee prices is shown below. In this case, the right whisker of the boxplot is much longer than the left (which has zero length because the lower quartile is equal to the lower extreme). This indicates right skewness. However, the left part of the box is much longer than the right part, indicating left skewness. It would therefore be misleading to describe this batch as either left-skew or right-skew. All you can really say is that it is certainly not symmetric.

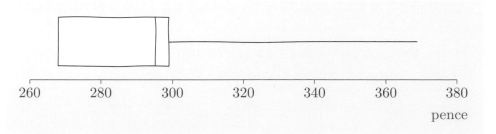

(c) The boxplot for the electricity prices is shown below. In this case, the right whisker of the boxplot is much longer than the left and the right part of the box is longer than the left part. Both these characteristics indicate that the batch is right-skew.

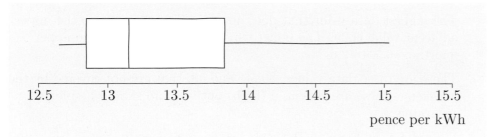

pence per kWh

Solution to Activity 13

(a) For the five-figure summary, you need the extremes, the quartiles, and the median.

The minimum is 6, and the maximum is 43.

For a batch size of 40, the median position is $\frac{1}{2}(40+1) = 20\frac{1}{2}$. The median is therefore halfway between the 20th and the 21st values in order. These are both 10, so the median is 10.

The quartile positions are $\frac{1}{4}(40+1) = 10\frac{1}{4}$ and $\frac{3}{4}(40+1) = 30\frac{3}{4}$. So Q_1 is one quarter of the way from $x_{(10)}$ to $x_{(11)}$ (where, as in Unit 2, $x_{(10)}$ means the 10th value in order, and so on). Here $x_{(10)} = x_{(11)} = 8$, so $Q_1 = 8$. Then Q_3 is three quarters of the way from $x_{(30)}$ to $x_{(31)}$, and here $x_{(30)} = 15$ and $x_{(31)} = 17$. The difference between these two values is 2, and three quarters of 2 is 1.5, so the upper quartile is $Q_3 = 15 + 1.5 = 16.5$, but (again, as usual in Unit 2), for presenting in a five-figure summary this should be rounded to the accuracy of the original data: $Q_3 \simeq 17$.

The five-figure summary is therefore as follows.

		10	
$n = 40$	8		17
	6		43

(b) The only extra calculations for drawing a boxplot are to find the interquartile range and hence the adjacent values. Remember to use unrounded numbers in intermediate calculations, and only round at the end.

$$\text{IQR} = Q_3 - Q_1 = 16.5 - 8 = 8.5$$

and so

$$Q_1 - 1.5 \times \text{IQR} = 8 - 1.5 \times 8.5 = 8 - 12.75 = -4.75.$$

The smallest data value that is not less than this is the minimum, 6, so the lower adjacent value is 6, and hence the lower whisker will go down from the lower quartile, 8, to 6.

$$Q_3 + 1.5 \times \text{IQR} = 16.5 + 1.5 \times 8.5 = 16.5 + 12.75 = 29.25.$$

The highest data value that does not exceed 29.25 is 29, so the upper adjacent value is 29. The upper whisker will go up from the upper quartile, 16.5, to 29.

There are three data values, 30, 41 and 43, that are not covered by the whiskers – these are potential (high) outliers and should be plotted separately.

In drawing the boxplot, the scale has to go at least as far as from one extreme to the other, that is, from 6 to 43. One possibility would be to have a scale running from 0 to 45, with the axis marked every £5, but there are other reasonable possibilities.

The resulting plot should look like the one below. (Yours might have a different scale marked on the axis.)

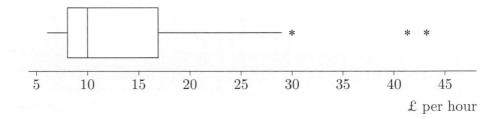

Boxplot of earnings for 40 female employees

Solution to Activity 14

(a) For the programmers:

$$\sum x = 465 + 484 + 620 + 654 + 855 + 858$$
$$= 3936$$

and the mean is

$$\overline{x} = \frac{\sum x}{n} = \frac{3936}{6} = 656.$$

For the others:

$$\sum x = 346 + 376 + 391 + 391 + 415 + 465 + 830$$
$$+ 843 + 876 + 1627$$
$$= 6560$$

and the mean is

$$\overline{x} = \frac{\sum x}{n} = \frac{6560}{10} = 656.$$

(b) The first batch size is 6, so the median lies halfway between the third and fourth value. These are 620 and 654, so the median is 637.

The second batch size is 10, so the median lies halfway between the fifth and sixth values. These are 415 and 465, so the median is 440.

(c) For the first batch, the positions of the quartiles are $\frac{1}{4}(6+1) = 1.75$ and $\frac{3}{4}(6+1) = 5.25$. Thus the lower quartile is three quarters of the way from the first value to the second value, so it is

$$Q_1 = 465 + \frac{3}{4}(484 - 465) = 479.25.$$

The upper quartile is one quarter of the way from the fifth value to the sixth value, so it is

$$Q_3 = 855 + \frac{1}{4}(858 - 855) = 855.75.$$

Thus

$$\text{IQR} = Q_3 - Q_1 = 855.75 - 479.25 = 376.5 \simeq 377.$$

For the 'others' batch, the positions of the quartiles are $\frac{1}{4}(10+1) = 2.75$ and $\frac{3}{4}(10+1) = 8.25$. Thus the lower quartile is three quarters of the way from the second value to the third value, so it is

$$Q_1 = 376 + \frac{3}{4}(391 - 376) = 387.25.$$

The upper quartile is one quarter of the way from the eighth value to the ninth value, so it is

$$Q_3 = 843 + \frac{1}{4}(876 - 843) = 851.25.$$

Thus

$$\text{IQR} = Q_3 - Q_1 = 851.25 - 387.25 = 464.$$

Solution to Activity 15

The completed table is as follows.

Data x	Mean $\overline{x}$	Deviation $(x - \overline{x})$	Squared deviation $(x - \overline{x})^2$
465	656	−191	36 481
484	656	−172	29 584
620	656	−36	1 296
654	656	−2	4
855	656	199	39 601
858	656	202	40 804
Σ		0	147 770

Solution to Activity 16

The completed table is as follows.

Data x	Mean $\bar{x}$	Deviation $(x - \bar{x})$	Squared deviation $(x - \bar{x})^2$
346	656	−310	96 100
376	656	−280	78 400
391	656	−265	70 225
391	656	−265	70 225
415	656	−241	58 081
465	656	−191	36 481
830	656	174	30 276
843	656	187	34 969
876	656	220	48 400
1627	656	971	942 841
$\sum$		0	1 465 998

The variance is

$$\frac{\sum(x - \bar{x})^2}{n - 1} = \frac{1\,465\,998}{9} = 162\,888.667.$$

The standard deviation is

$$\sqrt{162\,888.667} \simeq 403.6.$$

Solution to Activity 17

The completed table is as follows.

Data x	Squared data x^2
346	119 716
376	141 376
391	152 881
391	152 881
415	172 225
465	216 225
830	688 900
843	710 649
876	767 376
1627	2 647 129
$\sum$ 6560	5 769 358

Then the sum of the squared deviations is

$$\sum(x - \bar{x})^2 = \sum x^2 - \frac{(\sum x)^2}{n}$$

$$= 5\,769\,358 - \frac{6560^2}{10}$$

$$= 5\,769\,358 - \frac{43\,033\,600}{10}$$

$$= 5\,769\,358 - 4\,303\,360 = 1\,465\,998.$$

This is exactly the result you found for the sum of the squared deviations, $\sum(x - \bar{x})^2$, in Activity 16. As found in that activity, the variance is

$$\frac{\sum(x - \bar{x})^2}{n - 1} = \frac{1\,465\,998}{9} = 162\,888.667,$$

and the standard deviation is $\sqrt{162\,888.667} \simeq 403.6$.

Solution to Activity 18

To use Method 2 we need to know, for the combined batch, both of the following sums: $\sum x$ and $\sum x^2$.

These can both be obtained easily by adding the corresponding sums for the two separate batches in Table 16 and in the solution to Activity 17. Thus, for the combined batch, we have

$$\sum x = 3936 + 6560 = 10\,496,$$

$$\sum x^2 = 2\,729\,786 + 5\,769\,358 = 8\,499\,144,$$

and the size of the combined batch is $n = 6 + 10 = 16$.

Then, the mean is

$$\frac{\sum x}{n} = \frac{10\,496}{16} = 656.$$

Next, the sum of the squared deviations is

$$\sum(x - \bar{x})^2 = \sum x^2 - \frac{(\sum x)^2}{n}$$
$$= 8\,499\,144 - \frac{(10\,496)^2}{16}$$
$$= 8\,499\,144 - \frac{110\,166\,016}{16}$$
$$= 8\,499\,144 - 6\,885\,376 = 1\,613\,768.$$

So the variance is

$$\frac{\sum(x - \bar{x})^2}{n - 1} = \frac{1\,613\,768}{15} = 107\,584.533,$$

and the standard deviation is $\sqrt{107\,584.533} = 328.0$ (rounded to one decimal place).

Solution to Activity 19

The total number of red blood cells is $n = \sum f = 50\,000$.

The sum of the squared deviations is

$$\sum(x - \bar{x})^2 f = \sum x^2 f - \frac{(\sum xf)^2}{n}$$
$$= 14\,884 - \frac{11\,520^2}{50\,000}$$
$$= 14\,884 - 2654.208 = 12\,229.792.$$

Then,

$$\text{variance} = \frac{12\,229.792}{n-1} = \frac{12\,229.792}{49\,999} = 0.244\,6007.$$

The standard deviation is the square root of the variance, so it is

$$s = \sqrt{0.244\,6007} = 0.494\,5713 \simeq 0.5.$$

Solution to Activity 20

The required sums can be calculated as in the following table.

x	x^2	f	xf	x^2f
0	0	229	0	0
1	1	211	211	211
2	4	93	186	372
3	9	35	105	315
4	16	7	28	112
5	25	1	5	25
	$\sum$	576	535	1035

The mean is

$$\frac{\sum xf}{\sum f} = \frac{535}{576} = 0.928\,819 \simeq 0.9.$$

The sum of the squared deviations is

$$\sum (x - \overline{x})^2 = \sum x^2 f - \frac{(\sum xf)^2}{\sum f}$$

$$= 1035 - \frac{535^2}{576}$$

$$= 1035 - 496.918\,403 = 538.081\,597.$$

To find the variance, divide by one less than the batch size:

$$\text{variance} = \frac{538.081\,597}{575} = 0.935\,794.$$

The standard deviation is the square root of the variance, so it is

$$s = \sqrt{0.935\,794} = 0.967\,365 \simeq 1.0.$$

Solution to Activity 21

The quartiles were between the second and third values, and the eighth and ninth values, respectively, for this batch. None of these values have changed, so the quartiles have not changed either. Also, as the quartiles have not changed, nor has the interquartile range: it is still 464.

However, we must recalculate the standard deviation.

Data x	Squared data x^2
246	60 516
376	141 376
391	152 881
391	152 881
415	172 225
465	216 225
830	688 900
843	710 649
876	767 376
1727	2 982 529
$\sum$ 6560	6 045 558

The sum of the squared deviations is now

$$\sum(x - \bar{x})^2 = \sum(x^2) - \frac{(\sum x)^2}{n}$$

$$= 6\,045\,558 - \frac{6560^2}{10}$$

$$= 6\,045\,558 - \frac{43\,033\,600}{10}$$

$$= 6\,045\,558 - 4\,303\,360 = 1\,742\,198.$$

The variance is

$$\frac{\sum(x - \bar{x})^2}{n - 1} = \frac{1\,742\,198}{9} = 193\,577.556,$$

and the standard deviation is

$$\sqrt{193\,577.556} \simeq 440.0.$$

Solution to Activity 22

The value of the index in January 2001 as a percentage of its January 2000 value was

$$\frac{103.6}{98.2} \times 100\% = 105.498\,98\% \simeq 105.5\%.$$

Thus its increase over the year January 2000 to January 2001 was 5.5% of its January 2000 value.

Solution to Activity 23

(a) Real earnings for March 2011 compared with one year earlier is:

$$\frac{\text{AWE index for March 2011}}{\text{AWE index for March 2010}} \times \frac{\text{CPI for March 2010}}{\text{CPI for March 2011}}$$

$$= \frac{145.7}{142.8} \times \frac{113.5}{118.1}$$

$$= 0.980\,5671 \simeq 0.981 = 98.1\%.$$

(b) Real earnings for June 2011 compared with one year earlier is:

$$\frac{\text{AWE index for June 2011}}{\text{AWE index for June 2010}} \times \frac{\text{CPI for June 2010}}{\text{CPI for June 2011}}$$

$$= \frac{145.4}{141.3} \times \frac{114.6}{119.4}$$

$$= 0.987\,6488 \simeq 0.988 = 98.8\%.$$

(c) Real earnings for September 2011 compared with one year earlier is:

$$\frac{\text{AWE index for September 2011}}{\text{AWE index for September 2010}} \times \frac{\text{CPI for September 2010}}{\text{CPI for September 2011}}$$

$$= \frac{145.8}{143.1} \times \frac{114.9}{120.9}$$

$$= 0.968\,3038 \simeq 0.968 = 96.8\%.$$

Solution to Activity 24

(a) With earnings of £7500, Martha would not pay any tax and so her net pay would be £7500 before the increase. After receiving a 10% increase on £7500, Martha would receive

£7500 + £750 = £8250.

Tax on this would be 20% of £250, which equals £50. Therefore her net income would be £8200, which is a 9.3% increase on her previous net pay (rounded to one decimal place).

(b) With earnings of £8500, Martha would pay £100 tax and receive £8400 as net pay before the increase. After the increase her gross pay would be

£8500 + £850 = £9350.

Tax on this would be 20% of £1350, which equals £270. Therefore her net pay after the increase would be

£9350 − £270 = £9080.

This is an 8.1% increase on her previous net pay (rounded to one decimal place).

Solutions to exercises

Solution to Exercise 1

813 is the 80th percentile, so 80% of the men earned less than £813, and so 20% of the 10 652 000 men, that is, about 2 130 400 men, earned £813 or more.

Solution to Exercise 2

Here is the decile boxplot from Figure 10 with the key numerical values positioned.

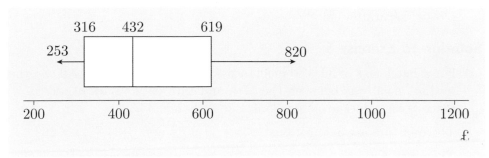

Solution to Exercise 3

As a percentage, the earnings ratio at the highest decile, for example, is

$$\frac{767}{966} \times 100\% = 79.399\,586\% = 79\% \text{ (to the nearest one per cent)}.$$

Calculating the other ratios in a similar way gives the following list.

Percentile	Earnings ratio
Highest decile	79%
Upper quartile	83%
Median	83%
Lower quartile	81%
Lowest decile	87%

The earnings ratio is noticeably higher at the bottom end of the distribution than at the top end. The ratios are fairly similar to those for jobs in all industries, as given in Table 8 (in Subsection 1.6).

Solution to Exercise 4

(a) For a batch size of 35, the median position is $\frac{1}{2}(35 + 1) = 18$. So the median is the 18th data value in order, which is 12. The quartiles are at positions $\frac{1}{4}(35 + 1) = 9$ and $\frac{3}{4}(35 + 1) = 27$. Therefore $Q_1 = 8$ and $Q_3 = 17$.

(b) Here IQR = $17 - 8 = 9$. So
$$Q_1 - 1.5 \times \text{IQR} = 8 - 1.5 \times 9 = 8 - 13.5 = -5.5.$$

There are no data values in Figure 19 less than -5.5 so the lower adjacent value is actually the minimum of the batch, 6.

Also,
$$Q_3 + 1.5 \times \text{IQR} = 17 + 1.5 \times 9 = 17 + 13.5 = 30.5.$$

The highest data value that does not exceed 30.5 is 29, so the upper adjacent value is 29.

There is only one data value, 38, that is not covered by the whiskers (that is, not between the adjacent values), so only 38 should be plotted separately.

Solution to Exercise 5

(a) For a batch size of 34, the median position is $\frac{1}{2}(34 + 1) = 17.5$. So the median is halfway between the 17th and 18th data values in order. Since these values are both 35.3, the median is 35.3.

The quartiles are at positions $\frac{1}{4}(34 + 1) = 8\frac{3}{4}$ and $\frac{3}{4}(34 + 1) = 26\frac{1}{4}$.

Therefore, the lower quartile is three quarters of the way between the eighth and ninth values in order, which are 30.1 and 31.7. The difference between these values is $31.7 - 30.1 = 1.6$, so
$$Q_1 = 30.1 + \tfrac{3}{4} \times 1.6 = 31.3.$$

The upper quartile is a quarter of the way between the 26th and 27th values in order, which are 36.7 and 37.5. The difference between these values is $37.5 - 36.7 = 0.8$, so
$$Q_3 = 36.7 + \tfrac{1}{4} \times 0.8 = 36.9.$$

(b) Here IQR = $36.9 - 31.3 = 5.6$. So
$$Q_1 - 1.5 \times \text{IQR} = 31.3 - 1.5 \times 5.6 = 31.3 - 8.4 = 22.9.$$

There are no data values in Figure 20 less than 22.9 so the lower adjacent value is the minimum of the batch, 26.1.

Also,
$$Q_3 + 1.5 \times \text{IQR} = 36.9 + 1.5 \times 5.6 = 36.9 + 8.4 = 45.3.$$

There are no data values in Figure 20 greater than 45.3 so the upper adjacent value is the maximum of the batch, 42.1.

In this case, no data values lie outside the adjacent values, so none are plotted separately.

(c) The boxplot is as follows. The two whiskers have the same length, suggesting that the data are symmetric. However, the left part of the box is longer which suggests that the data are left-skew. The general shape of the stemplot also indicates left skewness.

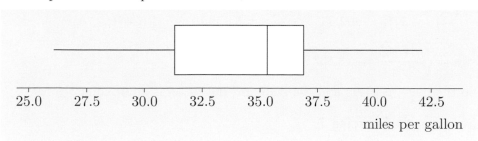

miles per gallon

Solution to Exercise 6

For the 'Before insulation' batch:

x	x^2
12.1	146.41
11.0	121.00
14.1	198.81
13.8	190.44
15.5	240.25
12.2	148.84
12.8	163.84
9.9	98.01
10.8	116.64
12.7	161.29
$\sum$ 124.9	1585.53

$$\overline{x} = \frac{\sum x}{n} = \frac{124.9}{10} = 12.49.$$

$$\sum (x - \overline{x})^2 = 1585.53 - \frac{124.9^2}{10} = 25.529.$$

$$s = \sqrt{\frac{25.529}{9}} = \sqrt{2.836\,556} \simeq 1.68.$$

So the mean is 12.49 and the standard deviation is approximately 1.68.

For the 'After insulation' batch:

x	x^2
12.0	144.00
10.6	112.36
13.4	179.56
11.2	125.44
15.3	234.09
13.6	184.96
12.6	158.76
8.8	77.44
9.6	92.16
12.4	153.76
$\sum$ 119.5	1462.53

$$\overline{x} = \frac{\sum x}{n} = \frac{119.5}{10} = 11.95.$$

$$\sum (x - \overline{x})^2 = 1462.53 - \frac{119.5^2}{10} = 34.505.$$

$$s = \sqrt{\frac{34.505}{9}} = \sqrt{3.833\,889} \simeq 1.96.$$

So the mean is 11.95 and the standard deviation is approximately 1.96.

Solution to Exercise 7

The required sums can be calculated as in the following table.

x	x^2	f	xf	$x^2 f$
0	0	27	0	0
1	1	44	44	44
2	4	26	52	104
3	9	3	9	27
$\sum$		100	105	175

The mean is $\dfrac{105}{100} = 1.05$.

The sum of squared deviations is

$$\sum (x - \overline{x})^2 = 175 - \frac{105^2}{100}$$
$$= 175 - 110.25 = 64.75.$$

To find the variance, divide by one less than the batch size:

$$\text{variance} = \frac{64.75}{99} = 0.654\,040.$$

The standard deviation is the square root of the variance, so it is

$$s = \sqrt{0.654\,040} = 0.808\,728 \simeq 0.81.$$

Acknowledgements

Grateful acknowledgement is made to the following sources:

Table 9 from the Office of National Statistics (2011) 'Patterns of Pay, 1997 to 2011 ASHE Results', reproduced under the terms of the OGL, www.nationalarchives.gov.uk/doc/open-government-licence/open-government-licence.htm

Table 11 from the Office of National Statistics (2011) 'Patterns of Pay, Annual Survey of Hours and Earnings', reproduced under the terms of the OGL, www.nationalarchives.gov.uk/doc/open-government-licence/open-government-licence.htm

Table in solution to Activity 11, from the Office of National Statistics (2011), 'Patterns of Pay, Annual Survey of Hours and Earnings', reproduced under the terms of the OGL, www.nationalarchives.gov.uk/doc/open-government-licence/open-government-licence.htm

Table 18 Wang C.C. (1970) *Transactions of the Royal Society of Tropical Medicine and Hygienc*, vol. 64, Elsevier Limited

Table 21 Clarke R.D. (1946) 'An Application of the Poisson Distribution', *Journal of the Institute of Actuaries*, vol. 72

Table 23 Bailey B.J.R. (1990) *Applied Statistics*, vol. 39

Table 24 taken from the Office of National Statistics, 'CPI and AWE Index Values in 2010 and 2011', reproduced under the terms of the OGL, www.nationalarchives.gov.uk/doc/open-government-licence/open-government-licence.htm

Figure 13 Rebecca Simpson / Dame Alice Owen's School, Potters Bar

Figure 17 taken from the Office of National Statistics, '2011 Annual Survey of Hours and Earnings'. Reproduced under the terms of the OGL, www.nationalarchives.gov.uk/doc/open-government-licence/open-government-licence.htm

Figure 21 US Federal Government

Figure 22 Courtesy of Londonist. www.londonist.com/2009/01/london_v2_sitemapped.php.

Figure 24 CPI Moto Limited

Subsection 1.2 cartoon (gender scales), www.cartoonmovement.com

Subsection 1.4 cartoon (median height), taken from www.medicine.mcgill.ca/epidemiology/hanley/tmp/DescriptiveStatistics/median_or_mean_height.gif

Subsection 1.4 cartoon (pay parade), Jeremy Banx / Banxcartoons.co.uk

Subsection 3.1 cartoon, Randy Glasbergen, http://www.glasbergen.com

Acknowledgements

Subsection 5.1 quote from the Office of National Statistics, 'Average Weekly Earnings (AWE) Index'. Reproduced under the terms of the OGL, www.nationalarchives.gov.uk/doc/open-government-licence/open-government-licence.htm

Every effort has been made to contact copyright holders. If any have been inadvertently overlooked the publishers will be pleased to make the necessary arrangements at the first opportunity.

Index

$\overline{x}$ 93
$\sum$ 93
∧-shaped   111
V-shaped   89
5-figure summary   118

absolute comparisons   175
adjacent values   201
all-commodities price ratio   131
all-item price ratio   141
annual rate of inflation   145
Annual Survey of Hours and Earnings   *see* ASHE
arithmetic mean   92
ASHE   178
Average Weekly Earnings   *see* AWE
AWE
    index   225
    measure   225

base date   131
basket of goods   133
batch of data   7
batch size   31
bimodal   50
boxplot   119, 121
    decile   189
    drawing a   204
    outlier   203
    skewness   199
    symmetry   123

chained price index   131
cleaning the data   16
commodity   101
comparing like with like   173, 185
Computer Book   5
Consumer Prices Index   *see* CPI
CPI   133

data   7
data collection   7
dataset   7
decile   188
decile boxplot   189
deviation   209
distribution   35

earnings   226
earnings distribution   180
earnings ratio
    at the highest decile   192
    at the lower quartile   192
    at the lowest decile   192
    at the mean   176
    at the median   180
    at the upper quartile   192
Equal Pay Act   174

first quartile   111
five-figure summary   118
frequencies   218

gender differential   171
goods and services   101
gross earnings   175
grouped data   217

Handbook   5
high outlier   38

index-linking   146
indexation   146
inflation   145
interquartile range   117
IQR   117

leaf of a stemplot   30, 31
left-skew   53, 199
level of a stemplot   30
Living Costs and Food Survey   135
location of a batch   36
low outlier   38
lower adjacent value   201
lower extreme   39
lower quartile   111, 112

M140 website   5
maximum   39
mean   92
    grouped data   220
mean of a combined batch   97, 98
measures of spread   39, 110
median   36, 88
minimum   39
Minitab   5
mode   49
model   7
modelling diagram   8
multimodal   50

observations   7
outlier   37

patterns   7, 29, 34
pay parade   183
PAYE   178

peaks   47
percentile   187
plagiarism   63
prediction   11
price ratio   127, 131
purchasing power   147, 148

Q_1 111, 112
Q_2 111
Q_3 111, 112
quartiles   112

range   39, 110
real earnings   230
relative comparisons   175
resistant   38, 95, 117
Retail Prices Index   *see* RPI
right-skew   53, 199
rounding   20
rounding error   22
RPI   133
    calculation   143
    groups   134
    weights   136

scatter of a batch   39
scatterplot   9
screencast   5
sensitive   95
shape of a batch   42, 47
significant figures   25
skew   53
skewness
    boxplots   199
    effect on mean and median   183
    stemplots   199

spread of a batch   39
spurious accuracy   19
squared deviation   210
standard deviation   209
    calculation   212, 215
    grouped data   220
stem of a stemplot   30
stemplot   30
stretched stemplot   44
sub-batch   91
    properties   92
summary measures   208
symmetry   51

tails   53, 188, 189
third quartile   111
truncation   37
tutor   6

unimodal   49
unordered stemplot   32
upper adjacent value   201
upper extreme   39
upper quartile   111, 112

variance   211

weighted mean   99
    of two numbers   103
    of two or more numbers   105
    physical analogy   99, 106
    rules   99
weights   99

year-on-year rate of inflation   145